MAN-HATER

To protect herself from the unwanted attentions of her friend Sue's objectionable husband, Kelly had hired herself an escort, in the person of Jake Fielding. And found she had jumped out of the frying pan into the fire!

MAN-HATER

BY

PENNY JORDAN

MILLS & BOON LIMITED
15–16 BROOK'S MEWS
LONDON W1A 1DR

First published 1983
Australian copyright 1983
Philippine copyright 1983
This edition 1983

© Penny Jordan 1983

ISBN 0 263 74403 5

Set in Linotron Times 11 on 11½ pt.
05–1083

Photoset by Rowland Phototypesetting Ltd
Bury St Edmunds, Suffolk
Made and printed in Great Britain by
Cox & Wyman Ltd, Reading

CHAPTER ONE

SHE must be getting old, Kelly thought tiredly as she snapped off the office lights. Time was when she had worked well into the evening and had still left the office with her batteries fully charged and her brain working on overdrive, but that had been when she had first started the agency off. Now that it was successful she was missing the challenge of those early days.

She sighed as she pressed the button for the lift. Her offices were in a prestigious block owned by one of the major insurance companies—clients of hers. The publicity work she had done for them had been so successful that she had been able to negotiate a very reasonable rent for the premises.

One of the reasons she had had to work late was that she had spent the morning with her accountant going over the figures for the company's current trading year. Ian Carlisle had been full of praise and admiration. The company looked set to turn in a record profit. 'And with the sound capital base it's had right from the start, you're in a very good position, Kelly,' he had told her.

Ian worked for the firm who handled her grandfather's affairs. He had been the one to shock her with the astounding news of her grandfather's wealth, shortly after his death. To find herself an heiress at eighteen had come so totally out of the blue that it had taken her quite some time to come

to terms with it. Kelly had never dreamed that
the grandparents who had brought her up in the
modest detached house just outside London had
possessed such wealth, and with hindsight she
doubted that even her grandmother had known of
her husband's predilection for the Stock Market,
nor his astounding success.

At first Kelly had been too overwhelmed by the
money to cope with the responsibility of it. It was
only later—after Colin—that she had become possessed by the need to make the money work, to
prove that women could be just as successful and
astute as men.

So why was it that she felt so depressed? By rights
she ought to be celebrating the company's third
birthday and its enviable success—not planning a
lonely meal in her apartment followed by an early
night after she had checked Sylvester's figures for
the Harding contract.

That success often equalled loneliness was something she was only just beginning to realise; but that
was what she wanted, wasn't it? Far better the
hard-won fruits of success than the perils of emo-
tional commitment—of relying on another human
begin. Since Colin she had not relied on anyone
other than herself—and that was the way she
wanted it, she told herself firmly.

Outside, the streets were empty of the rush hour
traffic. Success meant that one could not work a
mere nine-to-five day—but it had been worth it,
Kelly assured herself, barely giving her reflection
more than the merest fleeting glance as she glimpsed
her slender trench-coated figure in the store window. Kelly's was one of the most successful com-

panies of its kind in the city, and Kelly herself had the reputation of being a genius where getting good publicity for her clients was concerned. Top-class advertising agencies vied with one another to work alongside her, and she knew without a trace of vanity that the company's success was solely due to her own hard work and flair.

So why, tonight of all nights, was she in this oddly introspective mood? Why on earth was she questioning the quality of her life? The cost of total commitment to her career? She had made the choice, no one had forced her. After Colin she could simply have continued as she had done before; she was a wealthy young woman with no need to work. A form of therapy, Ian had once called it, and she wasn't sure if he wasn't right. And it had worked. So why was she feeling so restless? She was twenty-six; wealthy in her own right; commercially successful. She was attractive, intelligent, and had a close if small circle of friends. What on earth had she to feel restless about?

By the time she reached her apartment she had managed to throw off her earlier mood, and she unlocked her door with a small sigh of relief.

The apartment had been carefully chosen and decorated to reflect the image of the agency. The walls and carpet of the large living-room merged in matching softly grey blues; two large settees covered in off-white silk facing one another across a glass and stained-wood coffee table that matched the décor exactly, as did the silk-covered cushions heaped artfully on the off-white settees, in colours ranging from soft blue-grey to a rich deep azure. Kelly had employed the same firm of interior designers for the apartment as she had done for the office, and the result was a classical, if somewhat cold perfection. The apartment, as always, was impeccable. Kelly was lucky enough to have a first-class cleaner who came every morning to restore the apartment to its pristine splendour. Normally she enjoyed the cool remoteness of the living room with its gracefully modern Italian furniture, its 'touch me not' air of impeccability, but tonight, for some reason, it repelled her, and she found herself thinking instead of the house in Hampstead she had shared with Colin; of the bliss that had been hers for those few short months she had spent planning the décor—a décor far removed from the elegance of her apartment.

What was past was past, she told herself firmly as she shrugged off her trench coat in her bedroom, hanging it up as she had been taught to do by her grandmother, who had been a stickler for tidiness. She remembered that Colin had mocked her for this habit—as he had done for so many things, only at the time she had been too blind to recognise the truth for what it was, and had thought he was simply teasing her.

The excellence of her plain navy pin-striped skirt and white silk blouse spoke for themselves. The silk clung treacherously to the curves of her breasts— too generous in Kelly's opinion, and in the early days of the company she had had to freeze off the admiring looks of more than one client. Personally she thought her figure too voluptuous. Her waist was too narrow for the fullness of her breasts, her legs too long. If she had to find one word to describe her figure, that word would be 'flamboyant', Kelly

acknowledged distastefully, and she always dressed
in a style that minimised rather than maximised her
curves. Her hair was long and dark, and she normally wore it in a neat chignon. She had always
worn it long.

Her grandmother used to brush it for her every
night, and once released from its constraining pins
it had the texture and sheen of rich silk. She really
ought to have it cut, she thought, slipping off her
skirt and carefully returning it to its hanger, but
wearing it up helped to add to her air of reserve,
and this had been a useful weapon in establishing
the company. Men never tended to take seriously
women they were thinking of going to bed with
rather than giving a business contract to, and Kelly
had found out very quickly that her distant air,
coupled with her formal clothes and severe hairstyle, helped to preserve the image she wished to
maintain.

The day had tired her more than she had
thought. She had little appetite and longed only to
relax and go to bed, but first she had those figures to
check. She always changed her clothes when she
came home at night, never into the jeans and tops
she had favoured in the days before Colin, but
tonight for some reason something within her re-
belled and instead of reaching for the plain dress
she had been about to put on, Kelly found herself
removing from her wardrobe a richly patterned silk
kimono that one of her Japanese customers had
sent her the previous Christmas.

The azure blue background enhanced the darkness of her skin and the sapphire depths of her eyes.
Her skin was almost too pale—a result of not

having had a holiday for too long, she thought ruefully as she tied the sash, and removed the light layer of make-up she had worn during the day, brushing her hair methodically before returning to the living room and curling up on the settee with the papers she had brought home with her.

She was deeply engrossed in the figures when her doorbell pealed. Frowning, she went across to the intercom in the hallway and asked crisply to know the name of her visitor.

'It's me, Kelly—Jeremy Benson.'

Kelly's heart sank as she heard the familiar and, to her ears, faintly unpleasant drawl of her best friend's husband's voice. She had never liked Jeremy in the days when he and Sue were merely engaged, and her dislike had grown into loathing in the years that followed. Sue and Jeremy had been married for six years, and Kelly doubted that Jeremy had remained faithful to her friend for even one of them.

Sue and Kelly had been at school together. Sue was the closest friend she had, but ever since Jeremy had made it plain that he was sexually attracted to her, Kelly had found that she saw less and less of her friend, apart from brief shopping trips together, fitted in on Sue's infrequent visits to London, when Jeremy could not accompany them.

That Jeremy knew how she felt about him, and still persisted in his blatant attempts to seduce her, infuriated Kelly all the more and only reinforced her opinion of men in general, which was that as far as the majority of them were concerned, despite Women's Lib, and the much vaunted equality be-. loved of the newspapers, women were still *things* as opposed to people with equal rights, and that it was simply enough for a man to *want* and try to take, without having the slightest regard for the feelings, or lack of them, of the object of his wanting.

For Sue's sake, she had not told Jeremy how much she despised him. He was a weak and vindictive man and over the years she had seen him gradually alienate Sue from all her old friends, so that she was entirely dependent on him emotionally, while he was free to pursue his flirtations and affairs. Sue never mentioned Jeremy's failings to her, and Kelly genuinely believed that she was not aware of his real personality. She loved him, as she was constantly telling Kelly, and Kelly dreaded what would happen to her friend if she ever discovered the truth. Had she not had first-hand experience of the devastating effect such a discovery could have on a woman in love?

'Come on, Kelly, don't keep me waiting down here all night! I've got a message for you from Sue.'

It was on the tip of Kelly's tongue to tell him to simply give her the message and go, but she knew that, if she did, Jeremy would consider that he had scored against her. Jeremy was well aware of her aversion to him and, far from putting him off, it only seemed to increase his desire for her. If she refused to let him come up to the apartment he would goad her at a later date of being afraid to be alone with him; twisting the facts until it appeared that she was afraid to be alone with him because she desired him! Kelly knew quite well how his mind worked.

Her mouth twisting bitterly, she told him to come up.

His eyes widened appreciatively as she let him in, and as he bent forward to kiss her cheek, Kelly kept her body rigidly away from him.

He merely looked amused.

'Still the same old frigid Kelly,' he mocked. 'What's the matter? Afraid of what might happen between us if you really let go? No need to be, old girl.'

His manner, as always, set Kelly's teeth on edge and she could feel her temper simmering just below boiling point as she poured him a drink and handed it to him before sitting down opposite him.

'Fantastic place you've got here,' Jeremy said appreciatively, glancing round the room. 'Sue hasn't the faintest idea about décor,' he added disparagingly, 'but then, of course, I suppose everything's possible if one has the money.'

Two thrusts with one blow, Kelly thought acidly. First the criticism of her friend, and then the reminder that *she* had the wealth to buy good taste.

'You said you had a message for me from Sue,' she reminded him frostily.

'Welcoming, aren't you?' Jeremy complained, adopting a hurt little boy air that irritated Kelly beyond bearing, although she knew it worked well with poor Sue. 'We haven't seen you in months and now you can't wait to get rid of me.'

'I've got some work to do.' She indicated the pile of papers beside her. 'What are you doing in town anyway?'

Jeremy was an accountant with his own practice in the New Forest, where they lived, and it was a constant bone of contention with him that Kelly wouldn't transfer her business to his practice.

'A business meeting,' he told her. 'And Sue suggested I call and see you. She wants to show off the new house and suggested you might like to come down for the weekend. She's feeling a bit low at the moment, with the baby and everything.'

Was it *Sue* who wanted to show off the new house they had just bought, or Jeremy? Kelly wondered acidly, but the last part of Jeremy's sentence reminded her that her friend had just lost a much wanted baby, and it smote her conscience that apart from a telephone call she had not spoken much to Sue since the tragic event.

'What's the matter?' Jeremy asked, watching her craftily. 'Don't you fancy the idea? Or is it that you fancy it too much? There's something about you, Kelly. It really turns me on; the high-powered woman image. Poor Sue can't really hold a candle to you. She's developing into a boring little *hausfrau*, I'm afraid, and all this fuss about the baby hasn't helped.'

God, he really was callous and unfeeling! Kelly fumed, longing to tell him that in her opinion Sue was worth ten of him—at least. Part of her longed to refuse the invitation to refute his smug comments, but she valued her friendship with Sue and was suddenly conscious of the fact that her friend probably needed her company badly right now. If she refused there was no telling how Jeremy might react. He was vain enough to poison Sue's mind against her in the same way he had done with Sue's other friends, and she could not retaliate by telling Sue the truth—especially not now when she was bound to be feeling particularly insecure.

'I'll come,' she announced briefly, 'but you really

must leave now, Jeremy. I have to finish these figures tonight . . .'

She got up as she spoke, expecting him to follow her, but instead he reached up, caressing her hip, his gaze blatantly sexual as he stared at her body. A shudder of revulsion coursed through her, as Kelly pushed him away, her face taut with anger.

'All right, I get the message, but there'll be other times, Kelly,' Jeremy warned her. 'No woman, even a woman like you, can live the life of a nun for ever. See you at the weekend,' he added mockingly as she opened the door for him.

When he had gone reaction caught up with her and Kelly sank down on to the settee, her face a tortured mask of hatred and pain. God, the arrogance of the male sex! She loathed Jeremy's touch, and yet he assumed he had the God-given right to touch her, just because *he* wanted to!

Men! She despised them all! Frigid, Jeremy called her. Well, he was probably right. Colin had said much the same. Colin! She closed her eyes, unable to stop the shudders trembling through her. Dear God, would she never be able to forget?

She had met him just after her grandfather's death. He had worked in the same office as Ian, as a trainee accountant. They had met when Ian told her about her unexpected inheritance. At first she had been so overcome by the unexpected news that she hadn't even been able to think properly, and it was Colin who came running after her in the street with the umbrella she had left behind.

That had been the beginning; a fairly innocuous start to the events which had had such a cataclysmic effect upon her whole life.

It had been several days later when she received a telephone call from Colin at her office, asking her to go out with him. She had been drawn to him at first sight and had willingly accepted.

They went out for a meal and then on to a film. Colin had driven her back to her grandparents' house, where she still lived, in the old banger he had recently bought. He had kissed her goodnight, gently but determinedly, and her heart had sung with joy.

Six weeks later they were engaged. On Colin's advice she sold the house. He wanted them to have a completely fresh start, he had told her, but she had been startled when he took her to see the large house in Hampstead he thought they should buy. When Kelly protested that it was very expensive, he had reminded her that she was a very wealthy young woman and that anyway the house was an investment for the future, adding that when he had his own practice it would be useful for entertaining clients. Kelly had agreed, although Ian demurred a little when she told him of her plans, warning her that she would have to sell some of her investments to raise the capital.

Several hectic weeks followed. The house was huge and needed certain structural alterations; Colin was away on a course, and their meetings were only infrequent, restricted to discussions on progress with the house, and briefly snatched kisses.

Kelly had an aunt who lived in the north of England, in the Borders. She was Kelly's father's aunt really, and quite elderly, and Kelly had promised to visit her. She talked it over with Colin and it was arranged that she would go up for a few days before the wedding so that she could relax. 'You've been working so hard on the house, sweet,' Colin had told her, 'that you deserve a rest. I'll be away in Birmingham at our other office, anyway . . . Oh, before you leave,' he had added, 'I've got one or two papers for you to sign—nothing very important.'

She had signed them between kisses, wondering what it would be like to be really Colin's wife. Her grandmother had brought her up strictly and, a little to her surprise, Colin had made no attempt to press upon her any of the intimacies she had expected. Was he aware of how nervous she felt? she wondered as she travelled north.

Four days later she was back. She had enjoyed her stay with her aunt who, although well into her eighties, was hale and hearty. They had talked about Kelly's grandparents, and Kelly's father, who had been in the army and had been killed in Northern Ireland by a car bomb. Kelly's mother had been with him, and their orphaned daughter had been brought up by her grandparents. She had been four when her parents were killed and barely remembered them.

The wedding was to be a quiet one—a register office affair, although Kelly would have preferred to be married in church.

They weren't having a honeymoon—Colin had promised to take her away later when he had passed his final exams.

They returned to the house in Hampstead after a brief reception at a large London hotel.

Ian had been there and had kissed her cheek

gravely as he told her how lovely she looked.

They returned to the Hampstead house early in the evening. Dusk was just falling, and the drawing room looked pleasant and warm as Kelly snapped on the lamps. All at once she felt awkward and uncertain. Colin had gone upstairs, and she wondered whether she ought to go up too, or whether to wait to change out of her wedding suit until he came down. If only she had more experience! She dismissed the disloyal thought that Colin's manner was not very lover-like. Perhaps he felt as uncertain as she did herself, and she wished that their courtship had not been so brief and hurried.

'Bathroom's free if you want to get changed.'

She wheeled round, blushing a little as Colin walked in. He had changed into jeans and a sweater, and a tingle of excitement fired her blood as she looked at him.

'Colin . . .'

She paused uncertainly, willing him to take her in his arms and kiss her, to melt her doubts and fears with the warmth of his love, but instead he merely indicated the drinks tray on the table and asked if she wanted him to pour her one.

Shaking her head, Kelly went upstairs, telling herself that her let-down feeling was only nerves. Of course it was foolish to expect Colin to sweep her into his arms and make mad passionate love to her; modern people simply didn't behave like that.

She had just walked out of the bathroom when she heard the low hum of voices from downstairs. With no intention of eavesdropping she hesitated, wondering who on earth could have called on them tonight of all nights, when the drawing-room door

was suddenly thrown open and she heard Colin
saying angrily, 'Pat, I told you never to come here!'

'You also told me you loved me,' Kelly heard a
feminine voice reply. 'You told me you loved me,
and that this house was going to be ours—that you
would have your own practice and . . .'

Frozen with horror and disbelief, Kelly crept to
the edge of the stairs. Colin and his companion
were completely oblivious to her presence.

'And so we will, darling,' she heard Colin murmur softly. 'Everything will work out all right.'

'But you didn't have to marry her, did you?'
Kelly heard 'Pat' demanding angrily, 'God, Colin,
how could you?'

'Simple,' she heard Colin saying with new cynicism, 'I just closed my eyes and thought of all that
lovely money. Oh, come on, Pat,' he added, 'you
don't think I actually want her? God, she's the most
boring female I've ever known, a little brown
mouse and frigid with it. She can't hold a candle to
you, my sweet. The only way I can endure this
marriage is by telling myself that it's for us,
that . . .'

'But she's your wife!'

'Only for six months at the most. I've already got
her to sign the documents deeding the house to me.
Once I've persuaded her to give me the money to
set up my practice I'll tell her the marriage is over.'

Kelly felt sick with shock and disbelief. It
couldn't be true. But it was true! She only had to
look over the banister to see her Colin, her husband, with another woman in his arms, kissing her
with a hunger he had never shown her, to know
how true it was. Nausea welled up inside her and

she rushed back into the bathroom. The pair downstairs were oblivious to everything but one another and never even heard her.

Did Colin actually intend to make love to her? Kelly wondered sickly when the bitter spasms were over. And Pat, how did she feel about sharing her lover with another woman? How could *she* herself permit Colin to touch her knowing what she now did?

'Kelly? Darling, what are you doing up here?'

Kelly stared at Colin, wondering why she expected him to have changed.

He was still exactly as he had been before she discovered the truth; she was the one who had changed. She was no longer the foolish naïve child she had been then. Bitter fury welled up inside her.

'What do you want, Colin?' she challenged. 'My signature to some more papers, is that it?'

She saw the colour drain out of his face.

'Darling . . .' he blustered, 'I don't know . . .'

'I heard everything,' Kelly cut in coolly, marvelling at her own control. 'Everything, and if you think I'd allow you to so much as touch me now I . . .'

'Why, you sanctimonious little prude!' Colin snarled, slamming the door and walked towards her. 'Do you honestly believe I *wanted* to touch you? No way,' he told her cruelly. 'You've got nothing that appeals to me, Kelly. You can't hold a candle to Pat, you're frigid, or damn near, and . . .'

'I do have one thing you want—apparently . . .' Kelly interrupted acidly, hoping he wouldn't guess at the pain that tore at her insides. 'My money—

well, you won't get a penny of it, Colin. First thing tomorrow I'm having our marriage annulled!'

'Annulled?' He advanced to the bed, the cruelty in his eyes frightening her into rigid tension. 'No way,' he told her softly. 'I might not want you, Kelly, but I sure as hell want that money, and there's no way you're going to cheat me of it now. So you think you'll get an annulment, do you?' He laughed softly in his throat and terror stalked her as he stared down at her, slowly removing his sweater and then his jeans.

She wanted to run, but fear held her rooted to the spot, cowering on the bed, wishing she had the courage to get up and flee. The silk wrap she had put on after her bath was ripped from neck to hem in the degrading scene that followed, pain and fear locking Kelly's throat against the screams of terror building up there. Colin's hands bruised her body, just as his callous words had bruised her heart.

'Frigid bitch!' he swore at her, when her body clenched protestingly against him, hurt and frightened beyond any possible arousal, and he flung himself off the bed to stare furiously down at her.

'You're not a woman, you're an iceberg,' he taunted her as he pulled on his jeans. 'No one could make love to you—they'd freeze first!'

He was gone before she could speak, leaving her dry-eyed, her heart pounding with fear, her body aching with tension and the bruises and scratches Colin had inflicted upon it.

Frigid, frigid, frigid—the word danced jerkily through her mind as she lay there, unable to move, unable to cry, unable to properly comprehend. She heard the door slam as Colin left the house—going where—to Pat, who wasn't an iceberg, who wouldn't make him freeze? And then what? Would he come back and carry out his threat? Could she endure it if he did? Rape was an ugly word for an ugly deed, but that was what it would be if Colin consummated their marriage.

She was still lying there in the darkness when she heard the doorbell. She let it peal, until she realised that it wasn't going to stop. It had to be Colin, and she dressed slowly, hoping he would go away, but he didn't.

She unlocked the door, noticing that a false dawn was pearling the sky. She must have been lying there half-conscious for several hours, but it had seemed like only minutes since he left.

'Mrs Langton?' She peered up at the policeman standing on the doorstep. 'May I come in for a second?'

Somehow he had done and he was inside and asking where the kitchen was, saying something about a nice cup of tea. Kelly's numbed mind couldn't follow what he was saying, only that he was using a soothing tone, the sort one used on frightened animals—or children. Slowly, what he was saying sank it.

'Now, come and sit down,' he said gently, his own manner awkward and compassionate.

'He wouldn't have felt a thing,' he told her. 'Killed straight off . . .' He didn't add that his sergeant had said—and so he deserved to be, driving like a maniac on the wrong side of the road, with too much drink inside him.

Colin was dead! Why didn't she feel something?

Anything? She couldn't. All she felt was numb. She watched the young policeman with a curious sense of detachment. He seemed more concerned than her. He drunk the tea he had made quickly and asked her if she had any family.

She shook her head and heard herself saying clearly, 'It's all right, I shall be perfectly all right. Please don't worry . . .'

'Rum do,' the constable told the sergeant at the station later. 'Didn't so much as turn a hair.'

'Takes all sorts,' the sergeant commented, 'and news like that takes 'em all in different ways. Don't worry about it too much, lad,' he comforted the younger man—it was only his second 'fatal' and it was always hard to have to be the one to break the news.

Alone in the huge Victorian house, Kelly's own emotion was one of thankfulness. Of relief. Her love for Colin had gone, destroyed by the discovery that he had simply been using her. Her body ached from his cruelty, and her mind felt blunted and bruised. All she wanted to do was sleep. But there was one thing she must never do, and that was that she must never again be foolish enough to allow any man to deceive her as Colin had done. She must remember always that she was rich, that she was undesirable apart from her money and that she must always, always be on her guard. Always . . .

'Always . . .' With a start, Kelly realised that she had said the word aloud. Grimacing, she shrugged. She had come a long way from the girl she had been at eighteen. She was, after all, eight years older, eight years wiser. She glanced down at her hand where Colin's rings still glittered.

She wore them as a reminder; just as she used her married name. Since Colin's death she had learned that she *was* attractive to men, but she had never stopped wondering cynically why, and she thought she knew the answer. Those who were married simply wanted a few brief hours of escapism and thought they could use her body to achieve it, and those who weren't wanted to secure their future through her wealth and weren't averse to making love to her if by doing so they could achieve that object. She despised them all with equal fervour.

'A man-hater,' one of them had once called her, but didn't she have good reason to be? And hadn't Jeremy just confirmed that she was right?

CHAPTER TWO

SHE worried about the weekend when she should have been thinking about her work. There had been something in Jeremy's manner which suggested that he might be contemplating forcing the issue. A visit to her bedroom uninvited, perhaps? It had happened before—albeit not with Jeremy. And if she refused the invitation, how would Sue feel? Sue who had lost her longed-for baby before it was even born?

Kelly fretted over the problem for most of the day and left the office feeling jaded and tense.

She was half-way down a tube escalator when the advertisement caught her eye: 'Need a companion? An escort?' it asked. 'Phone us—we can provide either, male or female—to accompany you to that special function which you simply can't attend alone.'

Was it genuine, or was she being naïve? What was the matter with her? she asked herself as she hurried on to the tube. Surely she wasn't considering hiring an escort? But why not? It would be one way of keeping Jeremy at bay; and without the complications taking any other escort with her might involve. She had many male acquaintances, but there wasn't one of them who wouldn't leap immediately to the wrong conclusion if she suggested they spend the weekend with her.

She toyed with the idea all evening, alternately

dismissing and re-assessing it. It was ridiculous, farcical, but wasn't it also the ideal solution? There was nothing to be lost in simply making enquiries.

She dug out a telephone directory and searched through it. The agency had a surprisingly good address, a fairly new office block that Kelly knew quite well. She had contemplated taking a suite in it herself until she had received the offer from the insurance company for her present offices. Chewing her lip, she contemplated her alternatives. She could either go alone to Sue's and risk being proved right about Jeremy's attentions, or she could try and avert any unpleasantness by making enquiries at the agency and, if everything went well, employing one of their staff to accompany her.

Simple! So why should she be so wary and full of doubt? Was it because the idea of actually paying someone to accompany her smacked of a lack of femininity and—even worse—an admission that she could only attract male attention by paying for it? What did it matter? No one other than herself and the agency need know. Her motives were quite legitimate, and surely it was worth sinking her pride if it meant saving Sue pain and herself possible embarrassment. She had nothing to lose by simply calling at the agency and enquiring, had she?

As luck would have it, she had an appointment that took her in the vicinity of the agency's offices. She emerged on to the pavement from the impressively externally-mirrored building that housed the latest addition to their client list, sufficiently buoyed up with the success of obtaining a new and prestigious client to pluck up the courage to cross the busy street and walk purposefully into the

marble foyer of the building opposite. There was
no commissionnaire in evidence, but a quick glance
at the nameplates by the lift confirmed that the
agency was on the third floor. Feeling considerably
more nervous than she had done at her previous
interview, Kelly waited for the lift, smoothing the
skirt of her new Jaeger suit anxiously. The suit
wasn't something she would normally have chosen.
Maisie, her assistant, had persuaded her into it for
the meeting this morning. In a rich amethyst velvet,
the skirt fell in soft gathers from a neat waistband.
The jacket was faintly mediaeval, with a cropped
close-fitting collarless bodice and slim slightly
puffed sleeves, quilted with gold thread.

She was wearing a new blouse with it, cream silk
with a large collar worn outside the jacket, and an
amethyst velvet ribbon tied in a bow at her throat.

Somehow the outfit made her look faintly vulnerable rather than efficient; it even seemed to rob her
chignon of something of its normal formality.
Wisps of hair had escaped to curl round her tem-
ples, and Kelly toyed nervously with her pearl
earrings as she sent the lift to the third floor.

She saw the entrance to the agency the moment
she stepped out of the lift. The door to the foyer
was open and there was a man with his back to her
bending over a desk.

He straightened up as she knocked and walked
in, turning to study her with lazy appreciation.
Much to her chagrin, Kelly felt herself flushing with
anger as his glance slid potently over the length of
her legs in the sheer amethyst stockings that matched her outfit, pausing almost thoughtfully before
moving upwards, assessing the slenderness of her

waist encased in a broad suede belt, the full curves
of her breasts beneath the velvet jacket, coming to
rest with amused comprehension on her taut and
angrily flushed face.

'My apologies,' he drawled in a voice that, Kelly
told herself unpleasantly, sounded like all the
very worst television commercials, and was very
obviously less than sincere.

'Don't apologise if you don't mean it,' she snapped. 'Insulting me once was enough!'

'Oh? And how did I do that?' The husky voice
hadn't changed, but Kelly had the disconcerting
feeling that somehow she had angered him.

'By looking at me as though I were a piece of
merchandise you were considering buying. That
was your first insult,' Kelly told him scathingly.
'Your second was expecting me to be deceived by
your less-than-sincere apology.'

'Oh, I wasn't apologising for looking,' she was
told softly. 'What I was apologising for was embarrassing you.'

'Embarrassing me!' Kelly stared at him in fury.
Did he actually think she had been embarrassed by
his insulting scrutiny? 'You didn't embarrass me in
the slightest,' she told him coldly, 'you merely
annoyed me. How would men like it if women
stared at them as though . . .'

'As though they were pieces of merchandise they
were considering buying?' he quoted mockingly. 'I
don't know what brings you here, Miss . . .'

'Mrs Langdon,' Kelly supplied for him coldly,
watching his eyes narrow as he glanced at her left
hand as though seeking confirmation of her statement. 'I'm here for the very simple reason that I

wish to avail myself of the services of this agency,'
she went on tautly. Now that she was here, con-
fronting this arrogant specimen of manhood, she
was beginning to have grave doubts about her in-
tentions.

'The agency?' He glanced at the door, frowned,
tapping thoughtfully on the desk, while he subjected her to a provokingly intense study. 'You
mean the escort agency, I take it?'

'Is there any other?' Kelly snapped, her patience
worn thin by his manner and his scrutiny. He was
completely unlike the species of male she had
grown accustomed to over the years; they, well
primed as to her reputation and her wealth, were
normally either obsequious or respectful; sometimes flirtatious, but never, never did they regard
her with the cool disdain of this man, whose grey
eyes seemed to take her apart muscle by muscle,
assessing each and every part of her as he did so.
His hair was dark and brushed the collar of his
jacket—too long, she thought scornfully, but
doubtless there were some woman who found him
attractive. As far as she was concerned, he was far
too chocolate-boxy to appeal; he looked like one of
the actors one saw on television, driving lorries and
eating bars of chocolate or performing death-
defying acts on skis to deliver them. Some of her
contempt showed in the withering glance she gave
him, determined not to let his manner overset her.

'Umm . . . you're attractive enough, I suppose,'
he ventured calmly, 'but I scarcely think your manner is likely to win you friends or influence people.
If you really want a job I would suggest that . . .'

'*I* want a job?' Kelly broke in furiously, two

hectic spots of colour burning in her previously pale face. 'I haven't come here for a job, I've come here for an escort!'

'An escort?' If he was as stunned as he had sounded, he covered it up very quickly. 'I see, and just what sort of escort do you require, Mrs Langdon?' he asked smoothly, sitting down in the leather chair behind the desk, and pulling open a drawer. 'You must understand that this is a highly reputable and respectable agency, we don't . . .'

Kelly's furious gasp reached him and he straightened up, staring coldly at her. 'You're a married woman,' he pointed out.

'I'm a widow,' Kelly contradicted him, 'and I want to see the manager.' She threw the last comment at him through gritted teeth.

'By all means,' he agreed suavely, 'but you'll have to come back next week. He's on holiday at the moment.'

Next week! That would be far too late!

'Look, suppose you tell me your requirements . . . Do you need an escort for some official function?'

'Not exactly,' Kelly replied hesitantly, strangely reluctant to admit to this infuriating man exactly what she did want.

'I see. Well, perhaps if you were to tell me exactly what you do want . . .' He removed what looked like an application form from the desk and bent his head over it. His hair was thick and dark and possessed a glossy, healthy sheen, Kelly noticed absently. Why on earth had she come here? She longed to turn tail and run out, but simply didn't dare. His face was perfectly composed and polite, and yet Kelly had the suspicion that inwardly he was laughing at her. Well, let him laugh, she thought angrily, she didn't care what he thought.

Quickly she told him an edited version of her story.

'I see,' he said slowly, when she had finished. 'You wish to hire an escort to accompany you to a friend's home for the weekend. Your friend is married and you feel that a threesome might be awkward?'

That was what Kelly had told him, and she had no intention of saying any more.

'And you don't have any male friends who could accompany you?'

'Sue, my friend, is inclined to matchmake,' Kelly told him quickly, not without some truth. 'I thought it best if I took a complete stranger—to avoid complications later.'

'I see.' His expression told her quite plainly that he did not, but Kelly had no intention of enlightening him. However, several minutes later she realised that she had underestimated him when he said softly, 'This escort wouldn't be more of a bodyguard by any chance, would he?'

'Bodyguard?' Kelly looked at him sharply. 'Look, if you don't want my business, just say so.' She was beginning to lose her temper. Something about this man unleashed a powerful wave of antagonism she hadn't experienced in years. It must be something to do with the sexual magnetism that almost oozed from him—part of his stock in trade, she reminded herself scathingly, wondering what part he played in the agency.

'Not at all,' he responded smoothly, 'I was merely trying to discover exactly what you had in mind. You must appreciate that a legitimate agency such as ours sometimes receives enquiries it isn't equipped to handle.'

Kelly went brick red as the meaning of his carefully chosen words sank in.

'All I want is a male escort for the weekend,' she ground out with loathing. 'Nothing else!'

'Well, in that case, Mrs Langdon,' he continued with a briskness that belied his earlier words, 'if you will simply give me the details I'm sure we'll be able to sort out something.'

Coolly and concisely, Kelly told him. She thought she saw him hesitate when she gave him her address, and wondered cynically if he was mentally adding another nought to the bill she would be presented with. If so, he was in for a rude awakening.

'Will you require a car?' he said formally.

'I have my own,' Kelly told him shortly. 'Can you provide someone?'

She was filled with distaste for what she was doing, but she had come too far to back down now, and she faced him with dogged determination, trying to ignore the embarrassment and anger she was experiencing.

He studied her for a moment, then said slowly, 'How important is it to you that we do?'

It was on the tip of her tongue to tell him that it wasn't important at all, but somehow she found herself saying huskily instead, 'Very important.'

'Yes.' The grey eyes held hers intently. 'Yes, I

thought it must be. Now, what time do you want our man to be at your apartment?'

Quickly Kelly told him, only too glad to escape from the office ten minutes later, filling her lungs with steadily deep breaths as she stepped outside on to the pavement, only too glad to have the ordeal behind her. What was the matter with her? She had faced formidable Boards of Directors without flinching, and yet in front of that one man she had been reduced to a shivering, trembling wreck. Why?

For the rest of the day she found it difficult to concentrate. She had told Maisie that she intended to be away for the weekend.

'Take a couple of extra days off,' Maisie urged. 'You could do with the break. Go out and buy yourself a new dress.'

'I don't need one,' Kelly told her briefly, only somehow she found herself leaving the office earlier than usual, and as it just happened to be a late shopping night, she found herself wandering through the Knightsbridge stores; something that she hadn't done in ages.

She saw a dress that caught her eye on one of the racks. In crêpe satin by Calvin Klein, it was a deceptively simple wrap-round dress in a brilliant shade of pink.

Somehow she found herself in the changing room with it over her arm, discarding her velvet suit in order to try it on. The neckline plunged almost to the waist, the long tight sleeves hugging her arms in much the same way as the satin hugged her body, the fabric caught up in a knot just above the waist. It was hideously expensive and not the sort of thing she wore at all, and yet somehow she found herself buying it, even though she told herself that she was mad and it was simply not the sort of thing to wear for a quiet dinner in the country.

Sue rang her while she was still recovering from the shock of her spending spree.

'You are still coming, aren't you, Kelly?' she pleaded. 'I'm so looking forward to seeing you. I've been so miserable!'

Kelly could tell that tears weren't far away, and hastened to assure her friend that she would indeed be there.

'Jeremy will be glad to. I sometimes think lately that he finds my company very boring,' she heard Sue saying wistfully. 'Since the baby I've felt so down, and Jeremy always enjoyed the company of lovely women. I feel such a failure, Kelly . . . Here I am and I can't even produce a baby, and you . . . you have a fantastic career, the whole world at your feet . . .'

'Sue, you're not to think like that,' Kelly told her.

'I know—pathetic, aren't I? But I just can't help it. I feel so alone, Kelly, so frightened somehow. When do you plan to arrive?'

'Well, actually, it isn't just me,' Kelly told her hesitantly. 'Is it okay if I bring a friend?'

For a moment there was silence and then Sue asked excitedly, 'A man? Kelly darling, tell me all about him!'

Kelly laughed. 'Wait and see.' Well, she could hardly describe a man she hadn't yet met, could she?

Her information seemed to have had a dramatic

effect on Sue's mood, she bubbled and chattered in a way that reminded Kelly of a much younger Sue, and by the time she had rung off, Kelly was convinced that she had made the right decision, no matter what the cost to her own pride. She only hoped that the agency managed to produce someone presentable. She was a fool really, she ought to have asked to see a photograph and some background details, but she had been too flustered and angrily aware of her companion to do so.

Saturday morning came round all too quickly. The arrangement was that her 'escort' would present himself at her apartment on Saturday morning at nine o'clock. Kelly was dressed and packed by eight-thirty, her stomach fizzing with a nervous dread she hadn't experienced since . . . since Colin, really.

She inspected her reflection in the mirror once again. She was wearing her velvet suit, but this time her hair was caught back in a pretty gold-threaded velvet snood she had found in Liberty's and which added to the mediaeval effect of her outfit. It also had a softening effect of the severity of her hairstyle, and Kelly was frowning slightly over this when she heard her doorbell.

Picking up her case and bag and checking that she had her keys, she headed for the hall, opening the door and coming to a full stop, her mouth opening in a round 'Oh' of surprise as she recognised the man leaning indolently against the wall.

'You!'

He smiled as he took her case from her slackened grip and locked the door for her with the keys she had dropped in her agitation.

'What are you doing here?' Kelly demanded acidly, furious with herself for letting him take the initiative and treat her like a demented child.

'You wanted an "escort" for the weekend—here I am.' He shrugged casually and glanced at his watch, completely impervious to her anger. 'Shall we go? We'll make better time if we miss the morning traffic. The roads are practically empty at the moment. Are these your car keys?' He extracted them from the ring, handing her back her door keys with another smile, deftly pocketing the keys for her car as he motioned her towards the lift.

This couldn't be happening, Kelly thought dazedly. She wasn't used to men taking control of her life in this way, especially men like this one— men who cashed in on their physical attractions in order to make a living. The sheer discrimination of her own thoughts shocked her, but they couldn't be denied; somehow it was different for women to exploit their looks in order to make a living than it was for a man. Telling herself she was being ridiculous, she headed for the lift, wishing the agency had sent anyone but this man. She had disliked him almost at first sight that day in the agency's offices, and now she felt a resurgence of her dislike, hating the calm way he was taking over, robbing her of the control she always had of her own life.

When the lift stopped he stepped forward first, and Kelly seethed impotently, longing to push past him, but lacking the sheer brute strength, and sudden colour flooded her angry face as she realised he was simply ensuring that she wouldn't be caught in the lift doors. The expression in his eyes as she swept past him told her that he had guessed

the direction of her thoughts, and she flushed
again. The weekend had promised to be difficult
enough as it was, now it threatened to be intoler-
able.

'Why didn't you send someone else?' she muttered through clenched teeth to him as they entered
the underground car park. 'Or was the money too
much of a temptation?' she asked nastily.

She couldn't see his face, but the fingers cupping
her elbow tensed suddenly and his smooth, 'You
find man's very natural desire to provide himself
with a living contemptible? How odd. Or is it
simply the means by which I earn mine?' silenced
her. She had been betrayed by her own emotions
into making a judgment that was completely
biased, and he had underlined that fact.

'It seems to me,' he remarked pleasantly, as she
headed for the silver-grey Mercedes convertible
she had bought the previous year, 'that you have a
chip on your shoulder where the male sex is concerned. I wonder why?'

'Then don't!' Kelly snapped. 'That's not what
I'm paying you for.'

'You like reminding me of that fact, don't you?'
he continued evenly. 'Does it help to cancel out the
old wounds, Kelly, knowing that now you can make
the male dance to your tune?'

His words shivered across her skin, too close to
the truth for comfort, but she refused to acknowledge their accuracy, or the danger emanating from
the man standing at her side. How could a man like
this possibly be dangerous? He was simply someone whom she was using to prevent herself from
being trapped in a potentially difficult situation.

But he had used her name with an easy familiarity that had shocked her; and not just shocked. Hearing it on his lips had started a curious yearning ache deep inside her that she could neither define nor analyse.

'I was the only suitable candidate the agency had available,' he told her coolly, as they came to a full stop by the car. 'If you wish to change your mind and cancel the contract—then go ahead.'

Damn him, Kelly thought bitterly, he knew quite well she couldn't.

'Very well,' he continued, taking her silence for consent. 'In that case perhaps I'd better introduce myself properly. I'm . . .' he hesitated momentarily, 'Jake Fielding.'

'Jake.'

Somehow she found herself taking the hand he offered, her fingers curling instinctively at the first touch of the vibrantly male flesh against them.

He must have noticed her recoil, and she saw the speculation in his eyes as he bent to unlock the car door—the passenger door, Kelly noticed, as he swung it open and waited.

She looked up at him.

'You don't expect me to let you drive?'

'Why not? I have a current driving licence, if that's what's worrying you. You look tense and overtired,' he added unkindly, 'I thought you might enjoy an opportunity to relax before meeting your friends. Obviously you aren't looking forward to the weekend . . .'

'How did you know that?'

He looked surprised by her vehemence and shrugged. 'It's obvious, if you didn't need to feel on the defensive in some way you wouldn't have felt it necessary to hire me.'

There was no way Kelly could argue against such logic, and somehow she found herself slipping into the passenger seat while Jake put their cases in the boot and then came round to join her.

Whatever else she could say about him, she had to admit he was immaculately dressed, she thought, watching him discard the Burberry he had been wearing and toss it casually into the back of her car.

The fine beige wool trousers and toning checked shirt were exactly what one would expect to find a top executive type wearing in the country, as was the cashmere sweater he was wearing over the shirt, and Kelly had to repress a strange pang of pain as he started the car. It seemed so wrong somehow that with all her success and wealth she had to pay someone to accompany her to Sue's. What had gone wrong with her life?

Nothing, she told herself stoutly as the engine fired. She had everything she wanted; everything. Love was a chimera, she knew that; it didn't exist. God, she only had to look around her at her friends!

The automatic seatbelt device proffered the belt and Kelly reached for it automatically, shocked by the tingling sensation of hard male fingers brushing her own as Jake performed the small service for her.

She looked unwillingly at his hands. Dark hairs curled disturbingly against the wafer-thin gold wristwatch he wore. A present from a grateful customer? she wondered nastily, hating herself for

the thought, and hating even more the strange pain
that accompanied it.

'All set?'

She nodded briefly, reminding herself that Jake
was simply a means of protecting herself against
Jeremy—nothing more.

As Jake had predicted, they were early enough to
miss the morning traffic and once they were free of
London the roads were clear enough for Kelly to be
able to appreciate the beauty of a countryside
slowly awakening to spring. She had driven down
to Sue's before, but never along this route, which
seemed to meander through small villages and
open countryside and when she commented on this
fact, Jake merely said that since they were driving
to the New Forest the drive might just as well be as
pleasant as possible. He praised the car and asked
her how long she had had it, and yet there was no
envy in the question; if anything, his tone was
slightly amused and, nettled, Kelly responded coolly that she had bought it six months previously—as
a birthday present.

She knew the moment the boastful words left her
mouth that they were a mistake.

'You bought it for yourself?' The pity in his eyes
made her long to cause him a corresponding pain,
but caution prevailed. What did it matter what he
thought? After this weekend she would never see
him again, and yet even though she closed her eyes
and feigned sleep she kept seeing over and over
again the pity in his eyes.

'We'll soon be reaching the Forest.'

The quiet words were pitched low enough to

rouse her without waking her if she had been
deeply asleep, and Kelly lifted her head, glancing
through the window, entranced to see the massed
bulk of the Forest ahead of them.

'Would you like to stop for lunch?'

'Sue is expecting us,' Kelly told him curtly. She
didn't like the way he kept insisting on taking
control. She was the one in control. Ever since
Colin she had had a dread of anything else.

His shrug seemed to indicate that it meant little
to him, and Kelly felt rather like a sulky child being
humoured by a tolerant adult.

'Tell me a little more about your friends,' Jake
instructed as the new spring greenery of the Forest
closed round them. 'How long have they been
married? Do they have any family? I'll have to
know,' he added when he saw her expression. 'If
they're to accept me as a genuine friend of your
they'll expect me to know something about them.'

Grudgingly admitting that he was right, Kelly
explained about Sue's miscarriage and consequent
depression.

'Umm, but that still doesn't explain why you felt
the need for a male companion. It obviously isn't to
boost your reputation with your friend or score off
against her in some feminine way.' He reduced
speed, and glanced thoughtfully at her with cool
grey eyes. 'Something tells me there's something
you're holding back.'

'I've told you all you need to know,' Kelly denied, uncomfortably aware of the assessing quality
of his gaze and the hurried thudding of her own
heart. She couldn't admit the shameful truth; that
she was using him as a barrier to hide behind,

because for all her much vaunted independence, there was no other way she could get it through Jeremy's thick skull that she was totally uninterested in him.

Sue and Jeremy had an attractive brick-built house not far from Ringwood. The Mercedes pulled up outside it shortly after one, and as Kelly climbed shakily out of the car, the front door opened and a plump, pretty blonde girl came rushing out, enveloping her in a warm hug.

'Kelly, love, you look fantastic!' Sue beamed up at her. Barely five foot two, her lack of inches was something Sue constantly bemoaned; that and her tendency to put on weight.

'And this . . .' she began appreciatively, glancing from Jake to Kelly.

'Jake,' Kelly introduced hurriedly. 'I hope you don't mind . . .' Her voice trailed away, high colour touching her cheekbones as Sue grinned delightedly, 'Mind? Kelly, you know me better than that. But why haven't you told me before? I know you must be someone special,' she confided to Jake, oblivious to Kelly's agitation and embarrassment. 'Kelly would never have brought you down here otherwise. I can't remember the last time I've ever known her spend a weekend with any of her . . . Ah, here's Jeremy,' she broke off as the front door opened again and Jeremy emerged.

'Darling, come and say hello to Kelly and Jake,' Sue smiled, and Kelly heard the note of uncertainty in her voice; heard it and shivered with apprehension when she saw the expression in Jeremy's eyes.

'Kelly.' He reached for her, his eyes hard. 'I

suppose I can't kiss you properly with your friend
here looking on.' He contented himself with a light
peck, but Kelly was conscious of Jake's interested
scrutiny. He was too astute, she admitted uneasily,
and there was something about the way he watched
her that she found unnerving. Perhaps he was an
out-of-work actor simply studying human reactions, and yet there was something in the look he
gave her as Jeremy released her and turned to
shake hands with him that told her his interest had
been specific rather than general.

'Come on inside,' Sue encouraged. 'Lunch is
ready—a cold buffet meal, that's all, but I'll take
you upstairs to your room first.'

Their room! Kelly froze and heard Jeremy saying
smoothly behind her, 'I've finally managed to persuade Sue to join the twentieth century and to
realise that consenting adults don't want separate
rooms.'

He had done it deliberately. Kelly could see it in
his eyes. She wanted to protest; she felt like a
trapped animal and knew that Jeremy was waiting
for her to retract, and then, astoundingly, Jake was
slipping an arm round her waist, drawing her back
against his body. She could feel the even beat of his
heart against her back, her body enveloped in a
protective warmth that made her eyes sting with
tears as he lowered his head and murmured against
her hair, 'What delightfully tactful friends you
have, my love! I confess I hate wandering about in
the darkness looking for the appropriate bedroom
door!'

CHAPTER THREE

LUNCH was a nightmare during which Jeremy alternately humiliated Sue with his deliberate cruelty to her and cross-questioned Jake with a condescension that made Kelly wince.

Jake himself seemed impervious to his host's insulting manner, parrying his questions with a calm ease that Kelly couldn't help admiring, almost against her will. Her heart was in her mouth when Jeremy asked Jake what he did for a living, but Jake didn't hesitate for a moment.

'This and that,' he murmured with an easy smile, and from Jeremy's scowl Kelly knew that he had gathered from Jake's careless comment that he was implying that he was wealthy enough not to have to work.

From then on the two men treated one another with cool hostility, and Kelly was glad to escape into the kitchen on the pretext of helping Sue with the washing up.

'That was a lovely lunch,' she complimented her friend. Privately, now that the initial glow of excitement occasioned by the arrival had gone, she thought her friend looked far too pale and listless.

'Do you think so?' Sue grimaced. 'I think Jeremy believes I should have made more of an effort, but we seem to be entertaining constantly at the moment.' She pulled a face. 'I feel so tired, Kelly,' she complained. 'I've tried to tell him, but he just doesn't understand—about anything.'

She gave a muffled sob, causing Kelly to put aside the teatowel and take her in her arms. Her private opinion that Jeremy was a creep and that her friend would be better off without him was something she couldn't voice, so instead she comforted her by saying slowly, 'You've had a bad time recently, Sue, you're bound to be feeling a bit under the weather. You need a decent rest.'

'That's what Dad says,' Sue agreed shakily, 'but Jeremy says it's impossible for us to get away at the moment. Dad has a villa in Corfu, he's offered to lend it to us for Easter, but Jeremy doesn't seem very keen.' Her face suddenly lit up. 'Kelly, I've had the most marvellous idea!'

Kelly's heart sank as she guessed the words trembling on Sue's lips, but it was too late to stop them, and to her consternation Jake walked into the kitchen, both hands full of empty plates, his eyebrows raised in query, as Sue burst out impulsively, 'Oh, and you too, of course, Jake, you must both come . . .'

'Come where?'

'I was just telling Kelly that my father has a villa in Corfu. He's offered to lend it to us for Easter— I'd love to get away, but Jeremy isn't keen. I was just asking Kelly if she'd come with me, but it would be fantastic if we could make up a foursome.' She pulled another wry face at Kelly and said frankly, 'In fact I think Jeremy would prefer a foursome.' Her eyes clouded as she admitted unhappily, 'He's grown so distant recently, Kelly, I sometimes think that perhaps . . .'

'The only thing you need to think about is getting well again,' Kelly headed her off, dreading hearing Sue put into words any doubts about her husband's fidelity.

'And you will come? Oh, please!' Sue begged, tears sparkling in her eyes. 'Both of you must come. I can still remember what it feels like to be so much in love that you can't bear to spend a moment apart, believe it or not. You must be a very special man, Jake,' she teased suddenly, blinking away the betraying tears. 'I never thought Kelly would allow herself to fall in love again after losing Colin so tragically, but the very fact that she's brought you down here proves me wrong, and I can't tell you how glad I am. He obviously wasn't the slightest bit deceived by that cool, efficient façade you hide behind, Kelly,' she teased her friend, but tears still glimmered in her eyes, and Kelly felt a pang of pain for her friend that overrode her own embarrassment. Poor Sue, losing her baby was something she was finding it hard to come to terms with, and Jeremy didn't help, she thought angrily. Couldn't he see how much Sue needed his care and reassurance, or did he simply not care?

'Kelly?'

'Er . . .'

'You haven't told Sue whether we'll be able to join her at Easter or not yet,' Jake reminded her.

Kelly flashed him an irate glance. Of course it was impossible that they could. He knew that. She bit her lip, unnerved by the look she saw in his eyes. This man was her paid companion, she reminded herself, and he had no right to be behaving in the way that he was. She bitterly resented his assumption of control, the smooth way in which he had pre-empted her right to dominate their relationship.

'I . . . I'm not sure if I can get away from the office, Sue,' she lied desperately. 'Can I let you know?'

She hated seeing the disappointment in her friend's face, but what could she do?

After lunch they went for a walk. The countryside around the house was lovely, but the walk was spoiled for Kelly by Jeremy's boorish manner towards his wife and his constant references to the financial status of the owners of the properties they passed. She stiffened at one point when Jake murmured softly against her hair, 'You and Benson ought to get on like a house on fire—you both believe that everything can be calculated in terms of money; the only difference between you is that you have it and he doesn't. I wonder why he didn't marry you?'

'Perhaps because he wasn't given the opportunity,' Kelly snapped. 'Anyway, I was engaged myself when Sue met Jeremy.'

'Ah yes, of course.' They had fallen a little way behind Sue and Jeremy, and Kelly hesitated, glancing up into the mocking face above her as she heard the question in the smooth, drawling voice. 'Colin! Sue mentioned a tragedy . . .' He saw her wince and said coolly, 'Believe me, I'm not prying or consumed by curiosity about your past, it's simply that I don't want to make any mistakes.'

'Very professional!' Kelly bit her lip when she saw his expression. It was useless telling herself that he had no right to be annoyed; she could tell that he was.

'Look,' he grated against her ear, grasping her arm and swinging her round to face him, his fingers bruising the soft flesh of her upper arm with their grip, 'I don't know when, where or why you started hating the male sex, nor am I in the slightest interested in your sexual hang-ups, okay? Now tell me about Colin.'

Kelly was too angry to reply. How dared he talk to her like that! she fumed. She would report him to his boss; why on earth had she been landed with him? She had wanted an 'escort' who would melt into the background, not this totally male creature who exuded male dominance and insisted on taking control.

'Well? Or do I ask Jeremy?' he threatened softly. 'Something tells me he'd be only too delighted to help me delve into your past.'

'Colin was my husband,' Kelly muttered, hating him more with every passing second. What on earth had happened to her much vaunted hauteur? Something about this man shattered all her defences; he was like a steamroller, she thought bitterly, either too hard or too dense to see he was trespassing where he wasn't wanted, and yet she had the unnerving impression that he knew exactly how much she resented his probing; his determination to lay bare wounds she desperately wanted to cover up.

'And?'

The gall of the man! She drew in her breath in indignation, stunned into silent shock as his mouth suddenly descended on hers, blotting out the spring

sunshine. A kaleidoscope of colours whirled between her tightly closed eyes, her entire body rejecting the male power of him, her mind silently
shrieking its bitter resentment. Every muscle in her
body tensed within the circle of his arms, her lips a
stubbornly tight line of denial, as the warmth
of his probed their curves. She opened her eyes,
damning him with corrosive hatred, willing him
to release her from the humiliation of the subjuga-
tion.

'Take it easy,' he murmured the words against
her mouth. 'Sue and Jeremy are watching. Unless
you want them to think we're in the middle of a
lovers' quarrel you'd better kiss me back.'

'Go to hell,' Kelly muttered back, wrenching
herself out of his arms and hurrying down the path.
Her whole body was bathed in a fine film of perspiration. She felt sick and shaken. She hadn't been
held like that since . . . since Colin, her mind
forced her to admit. It had been a shock, finding
herself in his arms like that, knowing herself incapable of breaking free without his tacit permission,
and the knowledge had been frightening.

'Everything okay?' Sue asked solicitously, when
she caught up with them. 'You look pale.'

Jeremy glared furiously at her and said acidly,
'Well, well, so the ice has melted at last! I don't
know how you've done it, old man,' he commented
to Jake when he caught them up, flinging his arm
casually but so firmly round Kelly's shoulders that
she couldn't break free.

'Done what?' Jake asked, his eyes never leaving
Kelly's pale face.

'Melted the ice maiden,' Jeremy said maliciously. 'We'd all begun to think she'd frozen so hard it would take a pickaxe to get through to her.'

'Jeremy!' Sue reproached, giving Kelly an embarrassed glance.

'Oh, it's all right, Sue,' Kelly retorted, forgetting Jake for a moment in the heat of her anger. 'I'm well aware that Jeremy thinks I'm frigid just because I don't jump in and out of bed with every man I meet.'

'See how fortunate you are,' Jeremy said nastily to Jake. 'Why, I'll just bet if it hadn't been for Colin, she'd still be a virgin; rich and innocent.'

She could feel Jake looking at her and knew that her cheeks were hot. How dared Jeremy talk about her like that! Her hands clenched in the pockets of her suede jacket. She knew why he was doing it, of course. He was trying to get back at her for bringing Jake with her, just as he had done when he suggested that Sue gave them a double room. Their room! She had forgotten about that. She worried at her bottom lip, and then told herself that she was being stupid. Jake was hardly likely to pounce on her simply because they were sharing a room. Even so . . . She glanced uncertainly at him, and was rewarded by a quick hug.

'Kelly can give her money away to charity if she likes,' she heard Jake drawl convincingly. 'As my wife, she'll be supported by me, and not the other way around.'

'Lucky Kelly,' Jeremy retorted. 'Well, if you're looking for a charity, darling, do look in our direction first. I wish I'd had the good sense to find myself a rich wife.' The look he gave Sue made Kelly long to demolish him with a few well-chosen phrases, but she had her friend to think of and so merely gave him an ice-cold glare.

Jake was an excellent actor, she had to give him that. That bit about supporting his wife had been truly inspired, and totally convincing. She watched him covertly. He looked convincing. He looked the type of man on whom a woman could depend totally and completely. What on earth was she thinking? He was probably an out-of-work actor, used to playing all manner of parts. She was *paying* him to appear convincing!

When they returned to the house, Kelly went upstairs to unpack. She had been hoping that Jake would accompany her, so that they could discuss the best way to save them both embarrassment in view of the fact that they would be sharing the room, but instead he remained downstairs talking to Sue, merely interrupting his conversation to smile warmly at her and say casually, 'Unpack for me too, will you, darling. Although, thank God, I won't be needing the pyjamas I packed after all.'

Sue grinned appreciatively. 'You're blushing, Kelly,' she teased. 'Now I really have seen everything!'

It didn't take Kelly long to unpack. She hadn't brought much with her, just the new dress she had bought to change into for dinner, plus a skirt and jumper to wear tomorrow, her underwear and a silk nightgown she had bought on impulse several months before. She eyed it doubtfully as she lifted the soft blue fabric from her case. There was nothing particularly indecent about it, but it was more frilly and feminine than the nightshirts she normally favoured, and now she wished she hadn't packed it.

When she went downstairs, she could hear Sue and Jake still talking.

'I'm so glad she's found someone like you,' she heard Sue saying, as she paused outside the door. 'She's had a hard time since Colin died. I'd begun to think she was too frightened to let herself care for anyone else. Of course, you'll know better than anyone else that behind that cool façade she's . . .'

Kelly pushed open the door, unable to bear listening to her friend saying any more. She couldn't look at Jake.

'Kelly . . . come and sit down next to Jake and I'll make us all a cup of tea. Jeremy's had to go out, but he won't be long. I've invited another couple to join us for dinner. One of Jeremy's clients. You'll like them . . .'

Kelly couldn't bear the tense silence that followed Sue's departure. 'I suppose you enjoyed hearing all that,' she began fiercely.

'Not enjoyed, precisely,' Jake responded. 'It was certainly enlightening.' His arm was stretched across the back of the settee, and he started to wind a loose frond of hair from her chignon round his finger.

'Don't do that!' Kelly hissed, jerking away and then gasping with pain as he refused to let her go. 'Don't touch me!'

'We're supposed to be lovers, remember,' he drawled laconically. 'Sue expects to come back and find us in each other's arms. Think back,' he taunted. 'Try remembering what it was like with Colin.'

Kelly couldn't stop herself. She went white, shaking with nausea as she did remember. Colin, wrenching her head round, pulling her hair, slapping her face. She wanted to be sick; to scream and cry as she hadn't done then; she was aware of the room starting to recede, of Jake's muttered imprecation, and then she *was* in his arms, struggling against their confines, hating the frighteningly male contact of his body—and yet in some strange way some part of her longed to simply acquiesce, to give in and rest her head against his shoulder, to draw comfort from the sheer solid maleness of him.

'Kelly!'

She was aware of the anxiety in Sue's voice as Jake responded for her. 'She isn't feeling too well, but it's nothing to worry about.'

'Darling, you must go upstairs and rest, can I get you anything?'

'I just felt faint,' Kelly assured her. 'Nothing much—I came out without breakfast and felt slightly carsick, but I'm all right now.'

'I think Sue's right, you ought to go upstairs and rest,' Jake cut in firmly. 'I'd come with you,' he added with a wicked twinkle, 'but somehow I don't think you'd get much sleep if I did.'

Sue grinned, enjoying her friend's embarrassment, but Kelly was glad to escape from the room; from Jake's too disturbing presence. Something about him frightened her; and yet what possible reason could she have for feeling so threatened?

In spite of her resolution she did fall asleep. Maisie was right, she thought drowsily, lying on the large double bed, she did need a rest. The thought of Corfu at Easter was tempting, but only if she and

Sue could go alone. She couldn't bear the thought of fending Jeremy off for an entire week.

The door opening woke her. She glanced up sleepily, her heart pounding with fear, as she saw Jeremy standing there, watching her knowingly.

'Nights too exhausting for you nowadays, are they?' he taunted. 'So the iceberg's finally thawed! You should have told me, Kelly, I'd have been only too happy to oblige. Who is this guy anyway? I've never heard you mention him before. If you'd wanted a lover you only had to tell me.' He was coming closer to the bed. Kelly knew she ought to get up, but her muscles were locked in remembered terror and dread, her eyes wild and haunted as she stared up at him.

'You're a very desirable woman, Kelly, in spite of that cold front that comes on so strong,' Jeremy continued. His eyes were on her breasts and Kelly felt her heart pound with terror as he reached out towards her.

'She's also *my* woman,' Jake's voice interrupted coldly from the open door.

Jeremy whirled round, glowering furiously. 'What the . . .'

'Sue's looking for you,' she heard Jake say contemptuously, 'so unless you particularly want to cause an unpleasant scene I suggest you leave—now.'

Kelly couldn't move; not even when the door had closed behind him.

'So that's what it's all about,' Jake commented quietly. 'Pity,' he added, his mouth thinning, 'I was just beginning to be intrigued by you, wondering what lay behind the mask, but it's all a ploy, isn't it,

Kelly; a façade behind which you can conceal your affair with your friend's husband? Have you no compunction about what you're doing?' he demanded angrily. 'Don't you think Sue's had a raw enough deal as it is? Can't you see what Benson is? Or don't you care?'

'You've got it all wrong,' Kelly choked, struggling to sit up.

'You think so?' One dark eyebrow rose cynically. 'It seems pretty obvious to me that the reason you needed an "escort" for this weekend was not so much to make up a foursome as to deceive your friend as to your real relationship with her husband.'

'No!'

'No? Then what?' he taunted.

'It was because of Jeremy, because I knew he . . . he wanted me,' she shuddered, 'that I wanted an escort. I couldn't disappoint Sue, as you say, she's been through too much, but I knew if I came here alone Jeremy would . . .'

'Try to make love to you?' Jake supplied, watching her with an intensity that was unnerving. 'And that was why you came to the agency?'

'Yes.'

'Umm.'

'You don't believe me?' Kelly was astounded to hear herself asking the question. What did it matter to her whether he believed her or not?

'Oh, on the contrary, I believe you completely,' he averred, 'but what does puzzle me is why a cool, controlled lady like you should act like a terrified innocent every time a man comes near her. You were petrified just then,' he reminded her, 'and I

only have to come within a yard of you and you
shrink away from me.'

'You're exaggerating,' Kelly lied nervously,
sliding off the bed. There was a look in his eyes she
didn't like. It was distinctly speculative, and more
. . . much more, she acknowledged, shivering with
a sensual awareness of all that the look he was
giving her implied.

'Let's just put that to the test, shall we?' Jake
murmured dulcetly.

'I don't know what sort of game you think you're
playing,' Kelly gasped, 'but may I remind you that
you happen to be in my employ, and that I could
report you to the agency for this!'

'Go ahead,' he invited, mocking her. 'It might
just be worth it.'

Before she could stop him he had reached her,
ignoring her stiffening muscles as his arms went
round her, one hand tracing the rigid line of her
spine, while the other deftly removed the snood
constraining her hair, his fingers sliding through the
silken weight he had released.

'Stop this!' Kelly ordered. 'Stop it right now!'

She saw him frown, his eyes darkening suddenly
as he exclaimed, 'You're frightened! I wonder
why . . .'

'I'm not frightened,' Kelly denied, 'I'm just
furiously angry. Who do you think you are? Just
because you're a man you think you can assume
whatever physical rights you choose to take—well,
not with me, I . . .' Her eyes blazed their defiance
up at him, her fists beating an angry tattoo against
the impervious wall of his chest.

'I've just saved you from a fate worse than death,

remember?' he taunted. 'Don't I get a reward?'

'What do you want?' Kelly demanded nastily, 'a bonus?'

'Why, you . . .'

It was too late to tell herself that she had gone too far, much too late to evade the bruising pressure of his mouth on hers, stifling her protests, cutting off her breath, as he ground her lips back against her teeth, making her feel faint with fear and pain, only her eyes mirroring her shock and bitter resentment.

'Kelly!' Her bruised mouth was released, and she winced with pain when his thumb brushed softly against its swollen fullness. 'God, I . . .'

'You wanted to hurt me,' she stormed at him. 'Well, you did. Satisfied? Is your male ego flattered by the knowledge that you can hurt me physically? You men, you're all the same!' she raged half hysterically. 'You . . .'

'No!' The harsh denial cut through her furious ravings. 'No, Kelly, we're not all the same. I'm sorry I hurt you.' He bent his head and she flinched, watching his eyes narrow and harden in some purpose she couldn't guess at.

'You made me angry and I got angry back, but it wasn't a deliberate attempt to hurt you. Hasn't anyone ever told you that any man is bound to act like that when a woman freezes in his arms? Didn't Colin ever tell you that?'

She went milk-white, her eyes dark with pain, her fingers curling against his shoulder.

'Kelly?'

'I . . .' She gasped as his mouth brushed the parted softness of hers, but it was too late to reject him. Her defences were already far too weak and it seemed far easier simply to lie passively against him, and give in to the gentle motion of his mouth against hers; teasing, and tantalising with a touch as gentle as butterfly wings, the moist warmth of his mouth stroking over the outline of her lips, encouraging them to soften and part to cling helplessly to the hard warmth of his; her mind reeling, spinning with the impact of what was happening to her.

'Kelly, are you all right?'

She was dimly aware of Sue's voice outside the door, of Jake releasing her slowly, his eyes holding hers, daring her to deny that she hadn't responded to him; that she hadn't—she shivered with the knowledge—actually for one brief second physically wanted him.

'Kelly!'

She made a superhuman effort to regain control of her senses.

'We're coming, Sue,' she called back to her friend. 'I'm fine now.'

'Kelly . . .'

Jake was watching her, and she sensed that there was something that he wanted to say to her. Could he have guessed how long it was since she had been kissed like that? How many years her starved senses had been denied the sensual contact they had just enjoyed?

'I must go . . . I . . .'

'Kelly, what is it you're so frightened of?' he asked quietly.

'Nothing,' she lied tautly. 'I'm not frightened of anything . . . Now, will you let me go,' she hissed, pulling away from him and heading for the door.

Was she going completely out of her mind? Allowing him to kiss her like that? What on earth was happening to her? She had been told she was frigid for so long that she had come to believe it, she acknowledged as she opened the door. She had thought herself impervious to the kind of sexual arousal Jake had just subjected her to, but she wasn't, and the knowledge terrified her. It was like looking in a mirror and seeing a completely different reflection from the one she was accustomed to. Jake had kissed her—once—and her body ached with a need she was terrified to put a name to. Why? Why now? and why, oh, why with this man who saw and knew far too much about her already?

'So you're Kelly's friend?' Jennifer Gordon eyed Jake appreciatively. 'Lucky Kelly!'

'Exactly my sentiments,' Sue admitted with a laugh. At the other end of the table Jeremy shot his wife a thin-lipped smile and said nastily, 'Sorry, darling—you couldn't afford him, could she, Kelly?'

Jennifer Gordon's cold blue eyes sharpened speculatively, and Kelly longed to dash the contents of her wine glass in Jeremy's over-fed and pasty face.

'My feelings for Kelly have nothing to do with her wealth,' Jake cut in coldly, and if Kelly hadn't known better she could have sworn that that was real anger she saw in his eyes, real intent behind the pointed comment, real desire in the look he bestowed upon her as he lifted her hand and turned it palm upwards, towards his lips, his brief caress where her pulse raced treacherously sending shimmering waves of reaction through her.

She wouldn't be sorry when the whole farce was over, Kelly decided later, smiling politely as the Gordons left. It was well after one, Jeremy was obviously and unpleasantly drunk, and Sue had borne his snide insults so bravely all evening that Kelly could have wept for her. Sue was worth twenty of her husband, Kelly fumed; how could she simply sit there and allow him to insult her, the way he had done?

Half an hour later she was on the point of going upstairs when Jeremy staggered out into the hall.

'I wish you luck of her,' he muttered to Jake, who was behind her. 'Frigid little bitch!'

Kelly was glad Sue hadn't been there to overhear him, and her face was still flushed with anger when she walked into the bedroom.

'I'm sorry about this,' she apologised in a stilted fashion to Jake. 'Jeremy's idea of a joke.'

He recognised the bitterness in her voice and glanced thoughtfully at her. 'Meaning that since he never loses an opportunity of calling you "frigid" he thinks he's punishing us both by telling Sue that we wanted to sleep together? You've been behaving rather strangely for a liberated and experienced lady.'

'Meaning what exactly?' Kelly demanded, suspecting that he was mocking her.

'Merely that I thought every woman knew these days that feminine frigidity is a myth put about by incompetent male lovers.'

His raised eyebrows invited her to comment and when she didn't he mused thoughtfully, 'Personally, I'm still romantic enough to believe that sex—no matter how excellent—lacks impact without the intensity of mutual desire—mutual love.'

Kelly stared at him in surprise. These were the last sentiments she had expected to hear him express.

'What's wrong? You know,' he added thoughtfully, 'there's something distinctly intriguing about you, Kelly. On the one hand we have the cool controlled career woman, who cuts emotion right out of her life; on the other we have the grieving widow who misses her husband so much that she can't bear to let another man near her. Something tells me the real Kelly is neither of those women. You could represent an irresistible challenge to some man, Kelly.'

'But not to you,' she parried dangerously, daring him to contradict her.

'Oh, I don't know . . . But that's not what you hired me for—or is it?' he asked softly. 'Is that what you wanted, Kelly? A man to share your bed without question or criticism; someone who you could simply pay to disappear when you'd grown bored with him . . .'

'That's a disgusting suggestion!' Kelly choked. 'If I wanted someone to go to bed with, I wouldn't have to resort to buying myself a man!'

'I wasn't suggesting you would,' Jake retorted quietly. 'I was merely implying that your inadequacies might prompt you to do as men do in similar circumstances—that is, you might prefer to pay for your pleasure; treat your partner as an object; a commodity who you could simply use and discard . . .'

Kelly wasn't listening; she hadn't heard more than the first few words.

'What inadequacies?' she demanded shakily. 'What do you mean?'

Jake shrugged. 'You know damned well what I mean, Kelly. You freeze every time anyone comes near you—you've been married; you're not a child; I don't know what it is that makes it impossible for you to react normally to men, but it's definitely there.'

Kelly didn't dare to respond. Instead, she picked up her robe and bolted for the bathroom. Hateful creature! How dared he imply that she might feel inadequate! If she didn't like being mauled and pawed by all and sundry that was only because she was choosy. She despised men . . . and she had every right to. She had proved that a woman could be every bit as successful, every bit as ruthless and determined . . . But what about the cost of proving it? Slowly she stopped undressing, shivering slightly. The cost had been high, she acknowledged. She trusted no one; shared her life with no one; neither lover nor family. She was completely and absolutely alone, and she was tired of telling herself that she preferred it that way.

She was glad that she had the privacy of the bathroom, and that she could run the water to drown out the sound of her tears. Not that there was much sound; they flowed silently and steadily, as though they had been dammed up for far too long, until she was too exhausted to do more than shower briefly and get ready for bed.

When she opened the door, Jake was sitting in an armchair apparently engrossed in a book.

'Ah,' he explained when she walked in. 'Bath-room free? What's the plan for tomorrow?' he asked casually, picking up the pyjamas she had laid on the bed, and a towelling robe. 'What time do you plan to leave?'

'After lunch,' Kelly told him expressionlessly, wondering why she should feel so affected by the fact that he had barely glanced at her. That was what they had arranged before dinner, wasn't it? That since they had to share a room, they would do so in a civilised and unfussing manner. At least, she amended, that was what she had arranged. Jake had merely listened grimly in a silence which she remembered now had been fraught with an odd sort of tension.

She heard the bathroom door close behind him as she unpinned her hair and started to brush it methodically. She hoped that before he emerged she would be in bed and feigning sleep. Not that she had any fears that he might attempt to touch her; his comments about her inadequacies had more than banished those, and her face burned fiercely as she remembered the look which had accompanied them! How dared he pity her! How dared he!

CHAPTER FOUR

KELLY moved restlessly in her sleep, tormented by
the ghosts who pursued her. Colin . . . mocking
her. Colin . . . hurting her. She cried out, twisting
desperately to escape the clutching hands she knew
from experience could cause such pain, suddenly
jerked from her nightmare as a light snapped on
and a husky voice growled sleepily, 'For God's
sake, what's going on?'

It took her several seconds to realise where she
was, who the voice belonged to, by which time Jake
too was fully awake, his face puzzled and concerned as he studied her.

'That was some nightmare,' he commented
briefly. 'Are you all right?'

She wanted to say 'yes', but the word stuck in her
throat. She sat up, shivering as she felt the chill
night air striking her bare back and shoulders,
unconscious of the terror trapped in her eyes as she
glanced nervously round the room.

'Would you like a drink? A cup of tea?'

A cup of tea! Oh, how she yearned for one.

'I'll go down and make us one. You stay here.'

'Us.' How intimate the small word sounded!
Kelly shivered when Jake left the room, without
him it seemed alien and empty, her nightmares
crowding back, dragging her back into the past.
Why, tonight of all nights, did she have to re-live
the horror of her wedding night? She had stopped

dreaming about it years ago, but tonight for some
reason the old nightmare had surfaced in all its
shocking intensity. She could almost imagine she
saw the bruises forming on her smooth flesh where
Colin had punished her. She moaned softly, her
eyes going blank, and she was shivering with reaction and terror when Jake came back, frowning as
he put the mug of steaming tea on the table beside
her, the bed depressing under his weight as he sat
down.

'Want to tell me about it?' His hand stroked her
hair back off her hot face.

'Your hair's lovely,' he told her unexpectedly.
'Like silk, and your skin's so pale.' His glance
lingered appreciatively on the outline of her breasts
beneath the flimsy fabric of her nightgown, his eyes
narrowing as she flushed darkly.

'You don't have to say that,' she told him jerkily,
trying to draw away, but his arm round her waist
constrained her.

'What?' He was frowning again. 'What don't I
have to say, Kelly?'

'You don't have to flatter me,' she retorted
tightly.

'I wasn't flattering you.' His voice was pleasant
but firm. 'Flattery implies that I was speaking with
some ulterior motive. I was simply stating facts;
that you have lovely skin and hair, which you
do.'

With his free hand he touched the shining length
of her hair, his thumb tracing the line of her shoulder. Delicious tremors of sensation slid over her
skin, and Kelly shivered again.

'You're cold.'

Before she could protest, she was drawn against him, her skin flushing heatedly as she realised that the smooth warmth she could feel against her back was his naked chest; for he had not worn the jacket of the pyjamas she had put out for him.

'Don't panic.' She could hear the amusement in his voice as it brushed her ear. 'I'm simply doing the gentlemanly thing and helping you to keep warm while you drink your tea. Here.' He reached forward and handed her the mug, but Kelly had to hold it with both hands, she was trembling so much; and it wasn't just her hands, her whole body was trembling, trembling so much that she was spilling the tea, and then suddenly weak tears were sliding down her face, and she was shivering and crying alternately, unable to understand what was happening to her.

'Kelly, for God's sake!'

Jake didn't sound amused now, and he didn't sound angry either . . . He sounded . . . concerned. But why should he be concerned about her?

She felt his hands on her arms, turning her, holding her against the warmth of his chest, her face buried in the curve of his shoulder, his hands on her back, stroking, soothing, calming her overwrought emotions, the murmurs of comfort she could hear above her head, the soothing sound of waves against a beach. She felt lulled and safe, warm and protected, and it came to her on a jolting tide of awareness that she didn't want to leave his arms. She wanted to stay there. She stilled, and lifted her head.

'Kelly!'

There was a raw note of warning in Jake's voice, and she realised for the first time that her breasts were pressed against the exposed flesh of his chest, their only covering the fine satin of her nightgown.

'Kelly.'

This time her name was a statement of intent, and although he gave her plenty of opportunity to do so, Kelly made no attempt to move away as he lowered his head, touching the stilled softness of her lips. Her eyes clung to his. This couldn't be happening, Kelly thought heatedly. She couldn't be in this bedroom, in bed with this stranger, letting him kiss her, wanting him to make love to her, but she was and she did, and she couldn't understand what was happening to her. Suddenly, she didn't want to understand, she simply wanted to touch and be touched, to be close to and part of another human being.

Her small choked cry was lost beneath the heated pressure of Jake's kiss, a potent, drugging kiss that blinded her to what shreds of reason she had left. Her arms crept round his neck, his smothered groan as the brief movement brought her breasts in closer contact with Jake's chest, activating a response inside her that urged her to press her body closer to his, to exult in the hurried throb of his heart as his hands moved to the neck of her nightgown, unfastening the small bows that fastened it, his eyes darkening as he held her gently away, pushing aside the fabric to expose the swollen peaks that had wantonly incited him to do just exactly that. Kelly couldn't believe her own behaviour. Her stomach muscles quivered in aching protest, not at what she was doing—no, what she ached for was Jake's possession; his desire and the knowledge that she was desirable and capable of arousing such a man.

'Aren't you going to take it off?' Her mouth was dry as she whispered the words, Jake's eyes darkening in acknowledging response as he murmured huskily, 'Just try and stop me.' And then he was pushing aside the blue satin, and she should have felt embarrassed about the way he was studying her body, but all she could do was to try and control the fierce tide of exultation that swept her as she saw the dark colour running up under his tan as he studied her, and then he was removing his pyjamas, and she closed her eyes, seeing for a moment Colin, but it was only for a moment, for Jake was nothing like Colin, and her eyes widened in appreciation of his muscular masculinity, her fingers touching the tanned skin with tentative hesitancy as she became lost in a voyage of tactile discovery.

'Kelly, Kelly, what are you trying to do to me?' Jake groaned, the sound muffled against her throat as his tongue stroked over the sensitive skin, his hands exploring her body with a much surer touch than hers had on him.

She gasped as he pushed her down against the pillows, one hand tangling in the silky length of her hair while the other cupped one pale breast.

'I've been wanting to do this ever since you walked into that damned office,' Jake muttered 'thickly against her skin, and then Kelly was incapable of thinking, of breathing almost as he lowered his head, his tongue stroking urgently against her nipple, her mind reeling with shock and excitement as he savoured the arousal of her flesh, teasing it until she was almost lightheaded with the pounding ache of desire in her body.

'Jake!' She moaned his name despairingly, touching the dark hair, gasping her shock aloud as his hand slid over her hip and stroked her stomach, the sensations he aroused inside her as he sucked her throbbing breast spiralling wildly out of control until she couldn't contain them any more and she was clutching anxiously at his shoulders, her body arching willing beneath him, eager for the pleasure he was giving her.

'So good,' Jake muttered thickly as his lips caressed her breast. 'I've wanted you like this from the first moment I saw you.' He sounded almost drugged, his voice roughened by a desire that Kelly felt too. His free hand slid down to her hips, holding her against him, his teeth nibbling seductively at her sensitised skin, his body unashamedly aroused, and incredibly she felt a heated response; a need that burned through her.

The nightmare which had originally woken her was completely forgotten—everything was forgotten apart from Jake and the sensations he was bringing to life in her passion-drugged body. She responded to his touch with a feverish intensity that drove out everything else. She didn't know what subtle chemistry there was between them that made her react to him in the way she did, she only knew that it was there. She moaned, every nerve-ending tingling erotically, her body crying out for his possession. His hand touched her thigh, his lips murmuring her name hoarsely against her skin, and she shivered suddenly as the memories stormed back, and it was not Jake touching her, but Colin.

Colin who called her name and violated her body, her emotions.

She tensed instinctively, dimly aware of Jake lifting his body from hers, watching her, his eyes dark and hard.

'Kelly? What the hell is this?' he demanded tersely. 'What sort of game do you think you're playing?'

'Don't touch me,' Kelly moaned softly. She was shivering, tears filling her eyes, the past sweeping her inexorably backwards in time, and she shuddered in revulsion remembering how it had been; how Colin had hurt her.

'Don't touch you? Don't worry, I won't,' Jake bit out grimly. 'There's only one excuse—one permissible explanation for what you've just done. If you were a virgin I might . . . just might be able to understand, but we both know you're not. So why?'

'Colin,' Kelly muttered sickly barely aware of what she was saying. 'You reminded me of Colin and . . .'

The oath that ripped from Jake's throat silenced her, and too late she realised he had misunderstood. He stood over her, pulling on his robe, his face like granite, as he reached for one of the blankets, wrenching it off the bed.

'I never play substitute,' he told her icily. 'Never, Kelly. Got that? Oh, there's no need to look at me like that,' he added silkily, 'I don't get my kicks from using force. You're sick, Kelly. You're looking for a man who's prepared to play a part, who's prepared to be "Colin", but I'm not that man. The next time I touch you, Kelly, it will be because you ask me. Me . . . not Colin, not anyone else. Me!'

He was angry, furiously, bitterly angry. How
could she tell him that he was wrong; that it wasn't
like that? That just for a moment she had remembered the brutality of Colin's lovemaking, and the
memory had turned her from a warm, responsive
woman into a terrified numbed child? And what
about him? He had wanted her right from the start,
he had said, but wasn't that just exactly the sort of
polished line a man like him would use? How many
lonely, defenceless women had hoped to find love
in his arms? She shuddered again as realisation of
what she had been about to do swept over her. She
had wanted Jake with a physical compulsion totally
outside her experience, and he had played on that,
sensing her want, feeding it, but why? He was an
attractive, experienced predatory male; he was
also, she suspected, a poor one. The conclusions
were obvious—so obvious that she couldn't understand why she herself hadn't drawn them before!

Only another hour and then they could leave, Kelly
decided thankfully, glancing surreptitiously at her
watch. The weekend had been a complete disaster
in every way, and as for last night! She shuddered,
unable to stop her memory from playing back for
her a blow-by-blow repetition of the night's events.
What on earth had possessed her? There could only
be one word for it—lust! All the repressed desires
of all those years since Colin, and she hated herself
for what had happened. She would have preferred
to pretend that it hadn't happened, but the aching
throb of her swollen breasts reminded her all too
uncomfortably that it had.

'Kelly, you haven't been listening to me,' Sue reproached. 'I was just saying to Jake that it would be lovely if you could both join me at Easter.'

'*I* might be able to, Sue,' Kelly told her, forcing herself to pay attention, 'but I'm afraid it's impossible as far as Jake is concerned, isn't it, darling?'

'Oh, I don't know.'

She glared furiously at Jake, wondering what on earth he thought he was doing.

'I dare say something could be arranged,' he said smoothly. 'It's time I had a break.'

'But you said you were far too busy,' Kelly improvised wildly.

'Mmm, perhaps I'm having second thoughts. It's certainly a tempting prospect: you, me, the sun and the sea.'

'Quite the romantic, isn't he?' Jeremy sneered. An animosity had developed between the two men, brought on, Kelly was sure, by Jeremy's fury because she had outmanoeuvred him by bringing Jake with her. That at least had been the right decision and made everything else worth while. Sue looked a good deal more cheerful this morning, and Kelly shuddered to think what might have happened if she hadn't had Jake to keep Jeremy at bay.

'Oh, please say you will,' Sue implored, 'and it needn't be too expensive. Daddy is letting us have the villa rent free.'

'Sounds terrific,' Jake responded with a smile.

No doubt it did to him, Kelly thought sourly, all her previous doubts re-surfacing. Why was he encouraging Sue? To make sure he got a free holiday? What had been behind his behaviour last night? Her heart started to thump uncomfortably. She was a rich woman and a lonely one. Only she knew how close she had come last night to giving in to the most basic impulse of all human beings; the need to be close to another of their own kind. But what if Jake had sensed her need? He was a man who quite patently had expensive tastes and equally obviously did not have the means to indulge them. His clothes were expensive; surely he couldn't afford them out of the wages he earned from the agency? If he was an actor he wasn't a very well-known one; perhaps he had grown tired of waiting for the big break of playing the polished escort to rich women. Perhaps he had decided it was time he cashed in on his undoubted attractions? Why should she find the thought so disturbing?

'So you will come?' Sue sounded excited and Kelly dragged her mind back to the present.

'Of course we will, won't we, darling?'

'We will what?' she asked Jake suspiciously. He hadn't touched her this morning—at least not physically—he undressed her mentally every time he looked at her, and she seethed with bitter indignation as she watched him doing so.

'We will join Sue at Easter? We could both do with the break.'

'You may do, but I . . .'

'You do too,' Jake said firmly. 'After all, I could hardly go without you.'

Too true, she thought ironically. How could he afford it?

'I'm not sure, Sue,' she began, suppressing a gasp of pain as Jake gripped her fingers painfully, warning her not to go on.

'What was all that for?' she demanded angrily

when they were alone. 'I don't have the slightest intention of going to Corfu with you and you know it!'

'Why not? Do you prefer to remain in England—with Jeremy?'

'Jeremy!' Funny, but she had almost forgotten him; forgotten the reason she had hired Jake in the first place.

'Yes, Jeremy,' Jake mocked. 'Sue's husband. Surely you haven't forgotten him already? If you stay behind, he's bound to jump to the conclusion that you've done so because of him.'

It was true, and Kelly couldn't deny it. If she remained in London Jeremy would invent some excuse to come and see her.

'I don't know what you're trying to achieve by this,' she told him angrily, 'unless it's a free holiday!'

She had expected him to be angry, but instead he merely laughed. 'That helps,' he admitted, 'but there are other considerations.'

'Such as the fact that you're getting tired of being a paid companion,' Kelly hazarded wildly. 'Well, if you think . . .'

'How would you know what I think?' he goaded softly. 'And, Kelly—' She turned to glare at him. 'Try backing out of this,' he said softly, 'and I'll see that Sue gets to know the truth about her husband.'

Kelly paled.

'You wouldn't!'

'Try me,' he advised grimly.

'You're despicable, do you know that?'

'Then that makes two of us, doesn't it?' he said quietly. 'Or doesn't what you did last night come into that class in your book? Never mind,' he told her grimly, 'it does in mine.'

'You don't understand . . .'

'Then tell me,' he invited levelly, but Kelly couldn't say a word; couldn't betray to him now, in the cold light of day, the fact that she had withdrawn through fear and remembered pain. Only a virgin, he had said, and she wasn't that . . . but he was wrong, she was! And she was beginning to think she was destined to remain so for the rest of her life. Last night she had wanted him, this morning she was bewildered by the emotions he aroused in her.

Easter was less than a month away. Sue talked excitedly all through lunch of the holiday, while Jeremy sulked.

'That's right,' he goaded Sue. 'Go off and leave me while you enjoy yourself.'

'Why don't you come with us?' Jake interposed smoothly. 'Surely you could manage a few days?'

'Oh yes, darling, do,' Sue breathed.

'I might,' Jeremy muttered.

Less than an hour later they were on their way back to London. Kelly hunched furiously in her seat as she seethed inwardly at the way in which Jake had manipulated her.

'Sulking?' he asked trenchantly as they neared London.

'You had no right to accept Sue's invitation. Why did you?'

'Oh, I have my reasons,' he told her lazily, 'and like I said, don't try backing out, Kelly,' he warned her, 'or you know what will happen.'

'What are you looking for? It can't just be a free holiday.'

'Not just,' he agreed, smiling mockingly at her. 'Don't worry, Kelly,' he drawled as he manoeuvred the powerful car into another lane, 'I'm not Jeremy, and I have no intention of forcing myself on you.'

No, but he wouldn't need to use force, Kelly admitted, shivering a little. Had he guessed how much he had aroused her? She was rich and she was vulnerable—too vulnerable, and she only wished she knew what was in his mind.

He stopped the car an hour later outside her block of apartments, getting out and retrieving her case.

'I'll park this and then see you up,' he told her easily, not giving her the opportunity to refuse.

He was back within minutes, his hand under her elbow, as he guided her towards the lift.

'I'm perfectly capable of managing on my own,' she told him stiffly.

'Ah, but I must do the job properly.'

He saw her to her door, turning the key in the lock for her.

'The bill,' she began hesitantly. Would they invoice her, or did she pay now, or . . .

'Leave it until we get back from Corfu,' Jake advised her carelessly. 'Still,' he added thoughtfully, 'I don't suppose there's any harm in my taking a little something on account.'

He bent his head, his lips brushing hers lightly, mocking her startled expression.

'Why did you do that?' Kelly demanded when he had finished. 'You said . . .'

'I know what I said,' he agreed hardly, 'but perhaps I've decided to give you a second chance. See you at Heathrow.'

He was gone before she could respond. What did he mean? she seethed, as she walked into her apartment. *He* had decided to give *her* a second chance? A second chance of what?

She returned to her office on Monday morning, fully determined to put a call through to the agency and cancel the trip to Corfu, but when she reached the office it was to find that she had to fly out to New York urgently to discuss a new contract. It was ten days before she was back. She tried the agency several times but without getting an answer, resolving that she would just have to keep on trying until she did get through.

CHAPTER FIVE

'OH, I'm so looking forward to getting away,' Sue murmured, easing off her shoes. 'Aren't you?'

She had rung up the previous day to tell Kelly that she was coming up to London to shop and they had arranged to have lunch together.

'Jeremy is coming with us after all,' Sue continued without waiting for an answer. 'Kelly . . .'

Kelly's heart sank. There was a note in Sue's voice that warned her of what was to come.

'Kelly, I know you'll think I'm being stupid,' Sue got out in a rush, 'but I'm so worried. Jeremy's been so . . . so different since I lost the baby.' She produced a watery smile. 'I'd even got to the stage of wondering if there was someone else!'

'Then you're a fool,' Kelly told her firmly, mentally adding to herself, Who would be stupid enough to want Jeremy?

'Look, love,' she told Sue. 'Things have been difficult for you both lately. I know how much it hurt you—losing the baby . . .'

'Jeremy too,' Sue broke in loyally. 'Oh, I know he doesn't show it much, but he was looking forward to being a father . . .'

Kelly didn't know what to say. To murmur that there would be other babies seemed so crass somehow.

'I'm sorry, I told myself I wasn't going to moan on to you. How's Jake?' Sue asked, determinedly changing the subject. 'I like him, Kelly. He's so right for you somehow.'

Kelly smiled noncommittally. She had already decided to tell Sue that her 'romance' with Jake was off. Then she was going to telephone the agency and cancel the arrangements for Corfu. So Jake thought he could blackmail her into providing him with a free holiday, did he? He was in for a big shock!

'Oh, here's Jeremy,' Sue exclaimed, her face breaking into a smile. 'He said he'd try to join us if he could.'

Jeremy greeted his wife, and Kelly tried to conceal her distaste as he turned to kiss her, making sure it was her cheek that received the moistly unpleasant touch of his lips and not her mouth.

Jeremy ordered fresh tea for himself and Sue excused herself to go to the ladies', leaving Kelly alone with Jeremy.

'All set for Corfu, then?' he asked, leering at her faintly. 'How's the great romance? Shouldn't have thought he was your type, Kelly. Doesn't exactly strike me as the faithful sort either. Never mind,' he told her with another leer, his hand finding its way to her knee, 'I'm always ready to make sure you don't get too lonely. You've only got to say the word.' He was eyeing her speculatively, and Kelly felt sickened by the expression in his eyes. Were all men like this? Lusting after every woman who caught their eye with no thought of loyalty or respect?

'Pity he's coming to Corfu with us,' Jeremy added, his eyes narrowing as he watched her. 'So the ice-lady isn't quite as cold as she pretended to be. How did he do it, Kelly?'

Kelly was thankful that Sue returned before she had to answer. Jeremy sickened her, but he was still Sue's husband. She gritted her teeth, knowing now that it would be impossible to cancel the coming holiday. Jeremy had invaded the privacy of her bedroom once already—she wouldn't put it past him to try again. She was going to have to find an opportunity to tell Sue that this time she and Jake wouldn't want to share a room, although quite how she was going to do that she didn't yet know.

Her vulnerability to Jake's practised charm was something that astounded and terrified her. It was a galling admission to make, but she knew that she couldn't trust herself to resist him if he tried to make love to her again. She couldn't analyse what had happened to her; perhaps sheer old-fashioned frustration was the simplest answer; she was twenty-six and had never had a lover, had never wanted one, until now. She had once thought that Colin's treatment of her had frozen all her natural responses for good, but she had been wrong. In spite of his charm, his pleasant manners, and his obvious physical attraction, something about Jake frightened her; or was it her own reaction to him which was so terrifying?

Heathrow was a seething cauldron of humanity. Kelly searched desperately for Sue's familiar face amongst the crowds milling everywhere, wishing she had not had to come straight from the office to the airport. She felt hot, tired and grubby, uncomfortably out of place among these people in their obvious holiday clothes. She was wearing a wool and linen mix suit severely tailored, and a toning high-necked silk blouse. The temperature had started to rise during the day; she had had problems getting a taxi, and her suitcase felt uncomfortably heavy.

A light touch on her shoulder had her whirling round, her eyes darkening in bitter recognition as she saw Jake standing there. Unlike her he was dressed for the flight, in jeans which clung smoothly to the intensely masculine shape of his body, and a checked shirt open at the neck to reveal the dark hair shadowing his chest. Her heart in her mouth, Kelly could only stare at him, shocked by her own response to the intense masculinity of him. Eyes narrowed, he watched her. Did he know what sort of effect he had on her? She felt herself flushing as foolishly as any schoolgirl and turned angrily to lift her suitcase.

'I'll take that.'

'I can manage.'

'Who would dare doubt it?' His eyes mocked her. 'But we are supposed to be lovers, remember? Sue and Jeremy are waiting in the bar.'

He lifted her suitcase effortlessly, matching his long stride to her shorter one, indicating the bar where Sue and Jeremy were waiting.

'I'll get this checked in for you,' he told her. 'Sue's given me the tickets.'

Sue had made all the arrangements and Kelly had sent her a cheque for their tickets. Her mouth compressed angrily at his assumption of control, her body bristling with resentment. What was it

about him that affected her like this? Was it because he made her feel so vulnerable? So . . .
feminine? Was that why she had hired him? Because somehow the fact that she was paying for his
time gave her the upper hand, made her feel safer
—evened out the differences between them? Was
she afraid to give him any advantage over her? Was
she afraid of him? She shivered, not liking the
direction of her thoughts. Since Colin, she had
deliberately kept any involvement with the opposite sex to a bare minimum; in fact her male friends
were mostly older, well-married men; or younger
less sexually aggressive ones . . .

'What would you like to drink?'

She hadn't heard him arrive and jumped slightly,
her eyes widening as he placed his hand on her
shoulder, bending towards her, capturing her
parted lips and caressing them briefly.

'Mmm . . . nice,' he murmured as he released
her. She could feel Sue and Jeremy watching them
and flushed angrily. There had been no necessity
for Jake to kiss her like that. It was already well
established in their minds that they were lovers;
there had been no need for him to underline it. Her
lips tingled pleasurably, and she hated herself because she knew that when he kissed her she had felt
an almost irresistible urge to touch him.

They went through the normal boarding formali-
ties without any problems, and as the engines
warmed up Kelly experienced her normal stomach-
clenching fear. She had never been able to get over
her dislike of flying and she knew her nails were
digging into the arms of her seat, her eyes fixed
rigidly on the back of the seat in front of her.

She closed her eyes, willing herself to keep calm, not to give in to the fear clenching her muscles.

'So you are human after all,' Jake murmured against her hair. He lifted her hand from the seat arm, clasping it warmly between his. She wanted to pull away, but the plane started to move and her nails curled protestingly into her palm.

'It's okay, we'll soon be up.' Jake spoke soothingly, transferring one arm round her trembling shoulders, her face buried in the curve of his chest, his free hand still clasping hers. Beneath her cheek his body felt solid and muscular. She was suddenly aware of the warm masculine smell of him, the reassuring thump of his heart; the comfort of his arm holding her, protecting her . . .

What on earth was she thinking? This was a man who made his living from making himself attractive to women. The plane lifted, and she moaned a small protest, closing her eyes and clutching instinctively at the open neck of his shirt. And then they were airborne, and the pounding of her heart had lessened. The stewardesses were moving about, the relieved chatter of the passengers filtering through the tense silence of take-off.

'All right?' Jake asked matter-of-factly, releasing her.

'Fine.' She knew she sounded abrupt, but she hated him seeing and knowing her weaknesses.

'You really hate it, don't you?' he drawled sardonically.

Kelly glanced at him suspiciously.

'Tell me something. Have you ever relied on anyone, Kelly; let your defences down; given them your trust? Or did you bury all the normal feminine responses with your husband?'

'For "feminine" read "weak and vulnerable", I suppose you mean?' Kelly stormed back.

Jake was shaking his head, his mouth wry. 'No, that's what you mean, Kelly. When I say "feminine", I mean a woman's instinctive and very flattering need to lean on a male shoulder occasionally. Don't you ever stop to think how emasculating your attitude is, what a turn-off it can be? I pity the poor male who's fool enough to fall for you, Kelly, you'd never give him a chance, would you? You'd never let him be a man . . . or a lover.'

Her face was darkly flushed. Kelly hated him for what he was saying, but wasn't it true?

'I don't want a man,' she managed thickly at last, 'or a lover.'

'Why? Because no one could compare with Colin?'

'You're just like all the rest,' Kelly hit out wildly. 'You want a woman to be subservient, to . . .'

'What I want a woman to be *is* a woman,' Jake corrected. 'A woman isn't a man, Kelly, and that means she is neither inferior nor superior; she is simply different, and I personally wouldn't want it any other way.'

No, because he knew how vulnerable her sex was to men like him, Kelly seethed, men who used their sexuality to beguile and deceive, just as Colin had once deceived her into believing he loved her. All he had loved was her money!

Her head started to thump and she searched in her bag for some aspirins. When Jake saw her produce them he summoned the stewardess and asked for some Perrier water, handing it to her.

'I could have asked for that myself if I wanted it,' she snapped childishly.

His mouth thinned. 'As I am sitting nearer the aisle I simply thought I'd save you the trouble. You know what the problem is with women like you, Kelly—women who want to boss the whole world—they daren't let themselves be women; so they spend all their time fighting to overcome their sexuality, fighting to make themselves asexual. Have you ever looked at yourself—properly, I mean?' he demanded thin-lipped. 'Those clothes, the way you wear your hair . . . everything laced up tight and repressed . . .'

'What are you trying to say?' Kelly whispered back furiously. 'I'm a business-woman and my clothes and hair reflect my life-style.'

'Exactly, you're a cool hard lady, Kelly, and you like letting the world know it. But don't expect me to toe the line.'

'You're paid to toe it—remember!'

She watched the grey eyes darken to flint.

'Of course,' he agreed sardonically. 'That's how you prefer your men, isn't it, Kelly? Bought and paid for—obedience guaranteed. It makes you feel good, doesn't it, reminding me of your wealth . . . Be careful, Kelly,' he warned her. 'The road you've taken leads only to loneliness.'

'Perhaps that's what I want,' she retorted in a clipped voice, but inside she felt like crying; crying like a lost and frightened child, only there wasn't much point, was there? She had learned a long time ago that when she cried there was no one there to dry her tears, and the only person she could rely on was herself.

She must have slept—the effect of the headache pills, because the next thing she knew was that Jake was shaking her gently, telling her that they were coming in to land. She opened her eyes, flushing selfconsciously as she realised that she was in his arms.

He smiled sardonically. 'Don't worry about it,' he told her. 'Even Homer nods, so they tell me. Personally I'd hate to be you, Kelly, terrified of giving in to even the slightest human instinct . . . but then each to his own.'

Was that how she struck others? Kelly wondered as they left the plane. She knew that she had a formidable reputation at work, but then she was head of the agency and she had worked hard to build it up. She had to keep on top of things, otherwise she would lose everything she had worked for . . . But what was 'everything'? It didn't take too much of an effort to remember back to the days when all she wanted from life was a home and family, love . . . she pushed the thought away. Love! She ought to have learned by now that the love she had once dreamed of simply didn't exist. She only had to look at her friends. How many of them were really happily married? But at least they had had the courage to try; to commit themselves to another human being, whereas she . . . They hadn't experienced what she had, she reminded herself bitterly, they hadn't . . .

'Kelly?'

She realised with a start that Sue was watching

her anxiously. 'Are you all right?' her friend asked. 'You look so pale.'

'A headache,' she responded briefly. 'There was a crisis at the office before I left.'

'Good old Kelly,' Jeremy jeered. 'Always reminding us what a big business-woman she is! You've got a winner there, Jake. If I were you I'd give up work and let Kelly keep you.'

'You might just have an idea there,' Jake responded lazily. 'There's something very sexy about successful women.'

'Ignore Jeremy,' Sue whispered as they waited for the men to collect the luggage. 'I don't know what's got into him lately.'

Kelly did. He was trying to needle her, trying to humiliate her in front of Jake. Little did he know!

Two hire cars were waiting for them at the airport. They had decided on two at Jake's suggestion so that they could go their separate ways if they wished, and now that Jeremy had elected to join the party, Kelly was glad. Things were bad enough without the added strain of keeping up the fiction of devoted 'lovers' in front of Jeremy.

Sue knew where the villa was, having stayed there before, so they left first, with Jake and Kelly following.

The sun was blindingly brilliant and Kelly blinked painfully as she searched in her bag for her glasses. Unlike her, Jake seemed completely unaffected by the heat. Sue had told them that it was a four-hour drive to the villa and, since the small car did not have air-conditioning, Kelly wished she had had the forethought to bring a change of clothes with her for travelling—she could easily have

changed on the plane and her silk blouse was
sticking uncomfortably to her skin, her thick skirt
oppressively hot.

Jake, on the other hand, looked perfectly comfortable and relaxed in his jeans and shirt, and
Kelly envied him.

They were driving through a small village when
he braked suddenly, stopping outside a small
general store. At first Kelly thought there was
something wrong with the car, but anxiety turned
to irritation when he calmly climbed out and saun-
tered across the road to the shop. It was the kind
that seemed to sell everything, judging by the
articles hanging up outside. Jake disappeared into
the dim interior, returning five minutes later with a
parcel which he tossed across to her as he climbed
in and restarted the engine. 'A present for you,' he
said casually.

'What is it?' Kelly asked suspiciously.

'Open it and see.'

Inside the bag was a pretty pink crinkle cotton
dress; a tiered affair with shoestring straps and a
scalloped hem.

'I'll stop the car when we reach a quiet bit of road
and you can put it on,' Jake told her, apparently
oblivious to her expression.

'Put it on? I don't want to put it on,' Kelly told
him angrily. 'I . . .' She broke off as the car
screeched to an abrupt halt and Jake turned to her,
sparks of anger glinting in his eyes.

'Look, we've got a three-and-a-half-hour drive in
front of us with the hottest part of the day coming
up. Any woman with the slightest bit of sense
would have realised that before she set off and

dressed appropriately as Sue did. Look at yourself!
You're hot and you're uncomfortable . . . but if
you want to go on suffering, that's okay by me. I
simply thought you might feel cooler in that,' he
picked up the cotton dress, 'than what you're wearing.'

He was right, of course, Kelly knew that, and she
was behaving like a cross child. She was too hot,
and she should have had the sense to know that it
would be much hotter here than it was at home . . .
She bit her lip, turning away so that he wouldn't see
the glitter of tears in her eyes. What on earth was
the matter with her?

'You're right,' she agreed huskily. 'I'm sorry.'

'It's relatively quiet here,' Jake said coldly. 'I'll
get out and stretch my legs if you want to change.
Don't worry about us getting lost. I've been to
Corfu before and Sue's given me directions.'

So he'd visited Corfu before. Who with? Kelly
wondered curiously. Another 'client'?

She wriggled out of the straight skirt, keeping an
eye on his retreating back. He sat down on a rocky
outcrop, the wind lifting the thick dark hair, the
thin shirt stretched over the lean muscles of his
back. Her fingers trembled over the buttons of her
blouse. Oh, the bliss of taking it off! She frowned as
she realised that the bra she was wearing would
show under the strappy dress, and quickly took it
off. Her skin looked pale against the warm pink
cotton. Jake turned and seemed to be studying the
car, and she fumbled with the straps in her nervousness, tying them in clumsy bows. Jake started to
walk back and Kelly grimaced as she caught her
hair in the hook of her blouse, pulling out a few

pins. She glanced in the driving mirror, pulling a face when she saw how untidy she looked. Strands of hair hung down her back, her make-up was smudged and she felt sticky and grubby.

'Here, these might help.' Jake was opening the door, and handing her a pack of tissues. He seemed to think of everything, she thought wrathfully, dabbing at her sticky skin. The untidiness of her hair irritated her, and she pulled out the rest of the pins, rummaging in her handbag for her brush, dragging it ruthlessly through the tangled skeins of hair. She couldn't be bothered putting it up in a chignon again, but there was a rubber band in her bag and she used it to secure her hair off her face, quickly plaiting it, while Jake watched.

'What's the matter?' she demanded crossly, seeing the lazy amusement in his eyes. 'Surely you aren't going to tell me you haven't seen a woman brushing her hair before?'

'I was just marvelling at the transformation,' he told her drily, touching the long plait. 'You look about sixteen with this, although . . .' his eyes dropped to her body, and Kelly was suddenly conscious of the fact that her breasts were almost visible beneath the fine cotton and, worse, the effect his intent gaze was having upon her body.

'Feeling better now?' he asked, switching his gaze from her breasts to her hot face.

Grimly, Kelly nodded her head.

'You're going to have to do better than that, you know, if you're going to convince Benson that we're still lovers.'

The amused glance he gave her fired the anger that had been simmering inside her for so long.

'I didn't invite you to join me on this holiday,' she breathed bitterly. 'You blackmailed me into having you along. God alone knows why, although I think I'm beginning to guess!'

'You are?' The grey gaze narrowed on her face, watching her, making it difficult for her to breathe, hating the close confines of the car, hating the way he made her feel; the emotions his proximity forced to life inside her, emotions she did not want to feel.

'Enlighten me, then—let's see if you're right.'

He was still smiling, watching her with a lazy satisfaction that reminded her of a jungle cat toying with his prey, and fury boiled up inside her, the sheer pressure of her rage exploding through her normal caution.

'Well, let's just say if you're hoping I'm going to be a meal ticket for life for you, you're wrong, and forcing yourself on me for this holiday isn't going to change my mind! If you . . .'

'Stop right there!'

The ice-cold words cut through her tirade, and Kelly shivered nervously in the dangerous silence that followed.

'Let's get this straight. You think I'm after your money?'

'Well, aren't you?' Kelly challenged dangerously. 'You're obviously a man with expensive tastes.' She glanced disparagingly at his expensive Rollex watch, her eyes skittering away from him as she saw the molten anger banked down under the hard grey eyes.

'Lady, I feel sorry for you,' he grated, forcing her to look at him. 'You're really screwed up inside, aren't you? Is it because of what I am, or what you are, that you think you can buy me? Oh yes, you do think that,' he went on brutally before she could object. 'You must do. What is it, Kelly, can't you believe anyone would want you for your own sake? Well, I've got news for you,' he told her, his voice hard with contempt. 'There just isn't enough money in the world, never mind in your bank account, to make me want to marry you. I presume that *is* what all this is about?' He laughed harshly. 'My God, I don't think I'm really sitting here listening to this!'

Despite his sardonic manner, Kelly could sense the anger she had ignited within him, and it frightened her. He had no reason to feel angry, she reasoned. She had every right to think as she did . . . every reason . . .

'Then why did you insist on coming on holiday with us?' she demanded.

'Why?' He grimaced as though he had an unpleasant taste in his mouth. 'If I told you, you wouldn't believe me. If I had any sense I'd turn this car right round and get on the first plane back to the U.K.'

'Then why don't you?' Kelly challenged. 'I don't want you here.'

'You'd rather have dear Jeremy, is that what you're trying to tell me? If it wasn't for Sue I'd say the pair of you deserve one another, but she doesn't deserve to be hurt, and for her sake . . .'

For *Sue's* sake! Kelly felt as though someone had stuck a knife straight through her heart and was slowly, painfully turning it until she wanted to cry out with the agony it was causing her. What was the matter with her? What did this man matter to her?

By rights she ought to despise him, but he seemed to be the one who was full of contempt for her!

'What happened to make you so suspicious, Kelly?' Jake taunted as he set the car in motion again. 'Oh, I know you lost a husband; but people can only make allowances for so much . . .'

What would he say if she told him the reason she was so suspicious was Colin himself? She shuddered, wondering what was happening to her. She hadn't told anyone about Colin. Not anyone! Since the dreadful night of their wedding she hadn't allowed any man close enough to her to learn the truth, but Jake had got close to her . . . too close. Was that why she felt so antagonistic towards him? Did her antagonism really mask fear? Kelly wasn't a fool. If she was genuinely indifferent to Jake he simply wouldn't have the power to arouse the emotions in her that he did. She was frightened of him and she was frightened of herself, of her reactions to him. He had pushed open a door she had kept locked for too long, and her body still ached with the memory of how she had felt when he touched her.

Colour rushed to her cheeks as she remembered the abandoned way she had responded to his lovemaking. It had had an almost cataclysmic effect upon her, releasing the dammed-up springs of emotion, destroying for ever the myth that she was frigid.

The miles slipped by without Kelly being aware of them. She sat rigidly in her seat, conscious of Jake's tightly controlled anger; of the grim line of his mouth as they left the main road and began to drop through forested countryside, tantalising glimpses of the sea appearing here and there between the trees. Soon they were passing villas set amongst the trees, sugar almond colours, glimpsed through high walls.

They drew level with an open gateway, and Jake turned into it. Sue and Jeremy were just emerging from their hire car, and Sue came hurrying towards them.

'You made it, then!'

'Your directions were fine,' Jake assured her, giving her a warm smile as he switched off the engine. Pain ached through Kelly, tears stinging her eyes. What was the matter with her? Surely she couldn't be jealous of Sue? Jake was simply someone she was employing to keep Jeremy away, that was all, and she had never been the possessive type even with Colin.

'Kelly, you look pale,' Sue commiserated. 'Are you okay?'

'Just a headache,' Kelly mumbled. 'I'll be fine.'

She felt limp and washed out beside Sue, who seemed to have taken on a new lease of life all of a sudden. Jake climbed out and came round to her side of the car, opening the door while Kelly was still fumbling with the catch. His fingers brushed the curve of her breast as he helped her out and she recoiled as though she had been stung. Her body actually seemed to burn where he had touched her. She saw the sardonic expression in his eyes, the hardness of his mouth, and trembled without knowing why. Jake seemed to have changed—or was it merely that she was seeing him properly for the first time? She had angered him by telling him

that she thought he was interested in her money,
but surely it was a perfectly natural assumption, in
the circumstances?

'Come on, I'll show you to your room,' Sue told
her. 'Luckily Dad has staff who come in from the
village, so everything will be ready for us. There's
quite a British community round here,' Sue went
on. 'Business-men and so forth. Dad bought the
villa when he retired—you'll like it.'

Kelly did. It was larger than she had imagined,
and as she followed Sue through a large lounge, she
glimpsed the oval shape of a swimming pool
through the picture windows.

'There is a beach,' Sue told her, following her
glance, 'but the ground is rocky, and it's quite a
steep walk down. Here's your room.' She opened a
door, and Kelly walked inside. The room was a
good size, decorated in soft muted shades of coffee
and peach, with a window overlooking the cliffside
and the sea, which Kelly could just glimpse through
the pines. Single beds, separated by a white cane
table, and a couple of matching chairs were the only
furniture in the room.

'Bathroom off there,' Sue went on, indicating
one of a pair of doors. 'The other door is to the
dressing room. Sorry about the single beds,' she
added with a grin.

'Don't give it another thought.' Kelly hadn't
realised Jake was behind them. 'Personally, I don't
think there's anything cosier than sharing a single
bed,' he drawled, looking at Kelly.

She knew she was blushing, but couldn't do
anything about it. Why was it that those few words
conjured up such a picture of intimacy that her

whole body felt flushed with heat and excitement? She could picture all too easily how Jake might enjoy sharing a single bed; how his lean body would shape itself to that of his female companion, his arms holding her secure.

'I'll leave you to unpack. Dad said he'd arrange for a cold meal to be left for us—I'll just go and check.'

There was silence when Sue had gone. Kelly couldn't turn round for the life of her, even though she knew Jake was there. When he closed the door, the faint click sounded like a gunshot and she whirled round in shock.

'I would have thought this time you'd insist on separate rooms,' Jake told her cynically, his mouth wry.

'I would have done,' Kelly agreed tautly, 'but I didn't want to arouse Jeremy's suspicions.'

'Of course not. Although I should have thought someone like him would just suit you—he's married, so you needn't be frightened of him wanting your money, need you? So I'm to be your body-guard, am I?' he drawled, eyebrows lifting. 'Well, in that case, I'll have to make sure you get value for money, won't I? I don't want you feeling that you've been shortchanged, Kelly.'

'I don't know what you're so angry about,' Kelly told him.

'No?' His hard laugh held disbelief. 'You aren't that naïve, Kelly. Damn it all, you've handed me the worst insult a woman can hand a man, and you don't know "why I should be angry"!' he mocked acidly.

'It was a perfectly natural conclusion to draw,'

Kelly defended herself. 'Especially when you'd
. . .'

'I'd what?'

He was watching her with a look in his eyes that
made her wish she'd never started the conversation. She moistened her dry lips with the tip of her
tongue, her fingers curling into her palms, tension
drawn through her nerves like fine wire.

'When you'd . . . made love to me,' she finished
huskily. 'You . . .'

'Made love to you?' He laughed incredulously,
'Ye gods, where have you been? That wasn't
"making love", Kelly!'

No, it hadn't been, she knew on a savage burst of
pain. It had simply been the sort of thing a man like
him would do . . . almost as second nature.

'However,' he added grittily, 'since we were
interrupted when we were, it seems I owe you
something on account, and since I never like to be
indebted to anyone . . .'

He reached her with three lithe strides, one hand
shaping the back of her head, his fingers winding in
her hair, so that she couldn't move, the other
stroking the exposed column of her throat as he
gradually tugged her head back, his eyes watching
the play of emotions over her face.

A tremor of fear pulsed through her. Colin had
held her like this. She swallowed nervously, her
muscles tightening in dread as Jake bent his head.

'No!' She sobbed the word in panic-stricken
terror, watching the grey eyes darken and the firm
line of his mouth harden.

'No? Surely you aren't going to refuse me the
chance to repay my debts, Kelly?' he asked with

Love, romance, intrigue...all are captured for you by Mills & Boon's top-selling authors.

TAKE FOUR EXCITING BOOKS ABSOLUTELY FREE

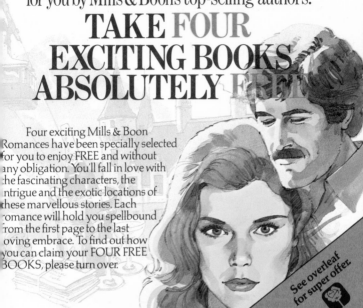

Four exciting Mills & Boon Romances have been specially selected for you to enjoy FREE and without any obligation. You'll fall in love with the fascinating characters, the intrigue and the exotic locations of these marvellous stories. Each romance will hold you spellbound from the first page to the last loving embrace. To find out how you can claim your FOUR FREE BOOKS, please turn over.

See overleaf for super offer

Mills & Boon, the world's most popular publisher of romantic fiction invites you to take these four books free.

FOUR BOOKS FREE

As a special introductory offer to the Mills & Boon Reader Service, we will send you four superb Mills & Boon Romances ABSOLUTELY FREE and WITHOUT OBLIGATION. Become a subscriber, and you will receive each month:

THE NEWEST ROMANCES – reserved at the printers and delivered direct to you by Mills & Boon.

POSTAGE AND PACKING FREE – you only pay the same as you would in the shops.

NO COMMITMENT – you receive books only for as long as you want.

FREE MONTHLY NEWSLETTER – keeps you up-to-date with new books and book bargains.

HELPFUL, FRIENDLY SERVICE from the girls at Mills & Boon. You can ring us any time on 01-684 2141.

THE FOUR FREE BOOKS SHOWN HERE ARE OUR SPECIAL GIFT TO YOU. THEY ARE YOURS TO KEEP REGARDLESS OF WHETHER YOU WISH TO BUY FURTHER BOOKS.

Just fill in and post the coupon today.

◘ Mills & Boon

Mills & Boon Reader Service,
PO Box 236, Croydon,
Surrey CR9 3RU.

NO STAMP NEEDED

✂ — — — — — — — — — — — — — — —

FREE BOOKS CERTIFICATE

To: Mills & Boon Reader Service, PO Box 236, Croydon, Surrey CR9 9EL.

Please send me, free and without obligation the four Mills & Boon Romances illustrated in this leaflet, and reserve a Reader Service Subscription for me. If I decide to subscribe I shall, from the beginning of the month following my free parcel of books, receive six new books each month for £5.70 post and packing free. If I decide not to subscribe, I shall write to you within 14 days. The free books are mine to keep in any case.

I understand that I may cancel my subscription at any time simply by writing to you. I am over 18 years of age.

Please write in BLOCK CAPITALS

Name_____

Address_____

_____

_____ Post Code_____

SEND NO MONEY – TAKE NO RISKS.   **XR 36**

One offer per household. Offer applies in UK only – overseas send for details. If price changes are necessary you will be notified

silky determination. 'You're not being very flattering, you know.' His lips captured the frantic pulse
throbbing beneath her skin, and instantly her fear
was gone, to be replaced by a languorous awareness of the pleasure being transmitted by the warm
male mouth as it moved sensually over her throat.

'Jake . . .'

She had meant his name to be a protest, but
somehow it sounded more like a plea. Jake
obviously interpreted it as such. His free hand
pushed aside the neckline of her loose dress,
caressing the curve of her breast. Instantly, Kelly
felt her nipples harden in excitement, her breathing
unsteady.

'Jake!' She tried to push him away, but her
fingers caught in the opening of his shirt, tangling
with the dark hairs on his chest. A molten fever
suddenly seemed to possess her, her senses blind to
everything but the warm silk of his flesh beneath
her fingers.

Jake's hand left her breast to find the hollow of
her back, holding her against him, the sensitive tips
of her breasts aroused by the intimate contact with
his body. His tongue stroked over her bottom lip,
her mouth parting achingly for his kiss.

She was being sucked down into a giddy whirl-
pool of pleasure, her whole world enclosed by the
heat of Jake's body and the pressure of his mouth
on hers. She arched helplessly against him, mind-
less in her desire to communicate to him her need.

When he suddenly released her the shock was so
great that Kelly clung instinctively to his shoulders.

'Oh no, Kelly,' Jake murmured slowly, his eyes
moving deliberately over her still aroused body.

'I've paid my debts. You hired me as a bodyguard, not a lover, remember.'

Nausea churned through her, humiliation a sour taste in her mouth. He knew that she had wanted him—he had deliberately aroused her just to prove to her that he could make her want him.

'I don't want you,' she lied bitterly. 'I could never want a man like you.'

'You're a liar, Kelly,' Jake told her softly. 'And you don't even begin to know the first thing about a man like me. One day you're going to stop living in the past with your ghosts, and you're going to admit that you're a real live woman, with real live emotions and feelings.'

He was gone before she could retort; before she could tell him that she would never feel anything for him. God, how she hated him, loathed him, loathed herself for responding to him! She walked blindly into the bathroom, shivering as she ran the water, but no matter how much she scrubbed her soft skin she couldn't wash away the memory of him touching her, caressing her, bringing her to life in a way she had never been before.

CHAPTER SIX

KELLY opened her eyes, tensing as she glanced at the motionless figure in the other bed, but Jake was still asleep, one brown shoulder visible above the thin cotton cover. She had been asleep when he came to bed. Her headache had grown worse during the evening and she had excused herself early, hating the mocking smile Jake gave her as she walked past him. Her body felt heavy and lethargic, aching with an emptiness she didn't want to acknowledge. Perhaps a dip in the pool would help refresh her?

Jake didn't stir as she slipped out of bed and gathered up her clothes. Their bedroom opened directly on to the patio by the pool, and Kelly slipped through the window as quietly as she could, expelling her breath slightly when Jake didn't move. She glanced at her watch; it was barely seven and she seemed to have the morning to herself. The air was pleasantly warm, small fluffy white clouds moving on the merest puff of wind.

The swimsuit she had put on was a new one—it had been years since she had last had a seaside holiday, and she had been pleased to discover an excellent selection of beachwear in the shops before her departure. She had been determined not to wear a bikini, but the swimsuit she had thought so sensible when she bought it was far more revealing then she had realised, dipping low at the front to

mould and accentuate her breasts and cut high at
the sides, lengthening her legs. If she had realised
how revealing it was, she would never have bought
it, Kelly decided, catching a glimpse of herself
mirrored in the azure water of the pool.

The water was pleasantly warm, and she swam
for several minutes before turning over to lie bliss-
fully on her back, paddling idly and letting the
tension flow out of her. It had been foolish to be so
concerned about her reactions to Jake. He was
after all a very handsome and experienced man, it
was only natural that she should feel some response
to him. It was unfortunate that he was here in Corfu
with them, but if she was sensible and level-headed
there was nothing to worry about. She bit her lip,
remembering his reaction to her accusation and the
swift reprisals which had followed. Her body quivered and she turned quickly, swimming strongly for
the side of the pool, dashing the water out of her
eyes as she pulled herself out.

'Good morning.'

A prickle of awareness shivered across her skin
as she looked up and saw Jake watching her. He
was dressed in cream jeans and a thin shirt opened
at the neck, and although he looked perfectly relaxed Kelly was aware of a difference in him. She
frowned as she tried to pinpoint exactly where it
lay; the nearest comparison she could come up with
was that he appeared to have changed from a
basking indolent jungle cat into a ferociously angry
predator deliberately stalking its prey.

He reached for her wrap before her, stretching
behind her to place it round her shoulders, his
hands lingering deliberately on her still damp skin,

tracing the shape of the bones beneath her skin. She shivered suddenly as her eyes met his and read the cynical message in their grey depths.

'Who chose the swimsuit?' he drawled, his eyes roaming with almost brutal sexuality over her body.

Kelly could feel her temper rising; resentment filling her.

'I chose it,' she gritted.

'Without trying it on?'

'What makes you ask that?'

'You look sexy in it.' He sounded quite bored, and looked it too, apart from the hard gleam in his eyes. 'Very sexy,' he added softly, 'sexy enough for me to . . .' His fingers tightened on her shoulders, pulling her hard against the length of his body, kissing her with a violence that robbed her of breath and even the will to resist. Her lips softened and parted and she was drowning in the sensual spell woven by Jake's touch, hungry for the feel of his skin beneath her palms. A fierce dry heat invaded her body and she didn't try to resist when Jake's lips left hers to explore the slim column of her throat. She couldn't understand what was happening to her, she thought, Jake only had to come near her and she melted; no, not melted, burned up, consumed by a heat that ached explosively through her body the way it was doing right now. So suddenly that it was a shock for her unprepared body Jake released her, lifting her hands from his chest to the lapels of her own robe where they trembled in rejection and humiliation.

'Hope I'm not interrupting?' Sue eyed her curiously and Kelly quickly tried to compose her-

self. 'I've just been having a swim,' she chattered
over-brightly. 'The water was lovely, Jake . . .'

'I came down to see what she was doing,' Jake
drawled laconically, propping his lean length up
against one of the patio tables, 'but the pool's a
little too public for the kind of swimming I prefer.'

Sue laughed. 'I came down to tell you that we've
been invited out to a party tonight. Some neighbours who know Dad, and hadn't realised that he
had lent the villa to us. They called round last
night, and when I explained that we were bor-
rowing they invited us all along instead. Should be
fun. The villa belongs to Carne Wrayman, the
television producer. He has a yacht which he keeps
here as well. His villa has its own private mooring.'

'Sounds fun, doesn't it, darling?' Jake murmured
before Kelly could speak.

'Oh, good. I'd better go and give Jeremy the
news. He'll be quite pleased.' Sue pulled a face.
'He'll look upon it as a good opportunity to get new
business. Don't worry about hurrying for breakfast. It's very much an alfresco meal—a help-
yourself affair really,' she added as she hurried
back to the house.

'She obviously thinks we want to continue what
she interrupted,' Jake mocked, when Sue had
gone. 'You'll notice that I don't charge extra for
these convincing little touches.'

'No, but you were quick enough to accept the
invitation to that party,' Kelly flashed back. 'You
don't deceive me. You may have given up where
I'm concerned, because you know I'm wise to your
game, but no doubt you're hoping to find someone
else to batten on to at the party—someone who

doesn't know the truth and won't know it until it's too late.'

'You're right about one thing, Kelly,' he said contemptuously at last when the silence between them stretched as fine as wire, and Kelly's heart was pounding with nervous exhilaration. 'Where you're concerned I have given up. You know, I felt sorry for you at first, but not any longer. You deserve everything you get. I'll let you use the bedroom first,' he added with deliberate cruelty, 'and you needn't look at me like that—I have no intention of touching you. In fact, judging by your reactions to me just then the boot is most definitely on the other foot.

'What's wrong?' he goaded, when he saw her stricken expression. 'Do you find it hard to admit you actually want a man like me? I sympathise; but sexual desire has nothing to do with logic, Kelly. You can't feed it into a computer and come up with exactly the right reaction to the right man.'

'I don't want you,' Kelly flung at him. 'I don't want you or any other man. Not now . . . not ever!'

'Fancy coming shopping with me?'

Kelly looked at Sue. 'I thought you said we wouldn't need to buy anything for the first few days.'

'Oh, not for food,' Sue assured her. 'I mean proper shopping—clothes, silly—or at least a dress for this do tonight. I haven't brought anything suitable with me.' She sighed, her expression suddenly sombre. 'In fact it seems ages since I bought myself anything pretty at all. I was so wrapped up in having the baby . . .'

They were alone on the patio. Jeremy had announced after breakfast that he fancied a game of golf and had coerced Jake into going with him.

'I've been giving myself a firm talking-to lately,' Sue continued briskly, 'and I've come to the conclusion that if Jeremy is finding me boring, I've no one to blame but myself. Daddy gave me a birthday cheque before we came away, and there are some excellent dress shops on Corfu. A great many wealthy Greek women live here, so most of the fashions are Paris inspired. You just wait and see!'

'In that case I'd better buy something new myself. I've only brought a couple of casual things with me,' said Kelly.

'And who knows—make a good impression and you could pick up some more business. Is it serious between you and Jake—settling down and getting married serious, I mean, Kelly?'

'I . . . It's too early to tell,' Kelly told her, hating having to deceive her.

'Well, he's certainly keen on you. You should see the way he looks at you when you're not aware of it!' Sue sighed. 'I envy you, Kelly. You have so much—oh, not your money, I'd never envy anyone that. No, it's the way you've proved to yourself that you can live alone; that you're your own person. I sometimes feel that without Jeremy I'd only be half a person; a shadow.'

'Nonsense,' Kelly told her firmly, 'but if it makes you feel any better I'll let you into a secret. There are times when I feel very much alone, when I wonder if I've paid too high a price for success, especially recently.'

'It doesn't show! Do you want to come shopping?'

'I think I'd better,' Kelly laughed. 'Are we going to drive?'

'Yes. It isn't very far, but the bus service is pretty haphazard. We'll take Jeremy's hire car.'

Half an hour later Sue deftly parked the hire car outside a row of shops, and Kelly climbed out. The sun burned into her skin through the thin blouse she was wearing, and she was glad that she had had the foresight to bring a hat and her glasses.

'Hot, isn't it?' Sue commented as she joined her. 'Let's try in here, shall we?'

The shop she indicated was quite small, a simple silk suit the only garment in the window. Inside, it was decorated in couture shades of dove grey and silver, and the woman who came forward to serve them had the timeless chic of the French.

Sue explained that she was looking for a dress to wear to a party. 'Something simple but stunning,' she smiled. 'Can you help?'

Several outfits were produced for Sue's inspection and finally she settled on a simple silk dress in a soft shade of lilac blue which suited her colouring. While Sue was trying it on, Kelly's eye was caught by one of the other dresses the woman had produced. Also made of silk, it had tiny shoestring straps and a low-cut back, the skirt cut on the bias so that it floated gently in the draught from the air-conditioning. In shades of pink from palest blush to deep cyclamen, Kelly knew instantly that it would suit her. She touched the fabric almost wistfully. Once she might have bought a dress like this, but not now.

'Ah yes, this is one of our exclusive models,' the saleswoman told her, walking over to her. 'Would you like to try it on?'

She was just about to say 'no' when Sue pleaded eagerly, 'Oh do, Kelly! You'll look stunning in it, I know.'

The trouble was that she did, and she knew it too, Kelly reflected rather wryly ten minutes later surveying her reflection in the mirror. The dress might have been made for her, it clung so lovingly to her body, making her skin glow like the inside of a oyster.

'It is very nice,' she began reluctantly, 'but . . .'

'No "buts",' Sue interrupted firmly. 'You're having it, and then you and I are going to treat ourselves to a couple of hours in the nearest beauty salon. We don't want Jeremy or Jake looking anywhere but at us tonight!'

The saleswoman, no doubt pleased to have made two good sales, gave them the address of a beauty salon which she recommended, and the girls there certainly seemed to know their business, Kelly thought approvingly as Helena, the girl who was looking after her, deftly produced a nail polish which picked out exactly the soft pink of her dress.

'If you don't mind me making a suggestion,' Helena murmured half apologetically as she worked expertly on Kelly's nails, 'I think your hair would look very pretty left loose for your party, perhaps swept to one side with a comb?'

'Oh yes, Kelly, it would be lovely,' Sue enthused.

Somehow, Kelly found herself being persuaded into the new hairstyle, which wasn't what she would have chosen herself at all. For one thing, the long dark sweep of hair, secured with a comb of mother-of-pearl, gave her features a sultry sensuality she had never expected. All at once her lips seemed fuller and softer, her eyes slumbrous and softly veiled. She looked . . . She looked as though she had just been passionately kissed, Kelly thought, startled by the knowledge.

'Kelly, you look fantastic!'

She gave Sue a vague smile. This wasn't how she wanted to look at all. Looking like this made her feel vulnerable.

Dusk was falling as they drove back to the villa. They had spent most of the afternoon shopping and then had a light meal, as Sue explained that she thought the men would eat at the golf club.

There was no sign of the other hire car when they returned. The party wasn't due to start until nine, which gave them plenty of time to get ready, Sue assured her, but Kelly decided that she would go to her room and get changed now—with luck she would be finished before Jake returned. What was the matter with her, she wondered ironically. They had shared a room; a bed; he had touched her and she had responded to him—and yet suddenly she felt afraid. But it was not the same sort of fear she had felt with Colin. Frowning and uneasy, she stripped off the clothes she had worn for shopping, securing her hair on top of her head as she went to turn on the shower.

Maisie had given her her favourite perfumed showering gel as a goodbye present, and Kelly used it lavishly. Even at her most austere she had not been able to deny herself the pleasure of perfuming

her skin. Colin had never bought her perfume and
so there were no unpleasant associations, but
tonight as she smoothed the gel over her skin and
stepped under the shower's fine spray, the fine
needles of water against her body seemed almost
erotic, the perfume released by the warmth of the
water clinging to her flesh. If she closed her eyes she
could almost imagine that Jake was touching her,
arousing her already inflamed body with his skilled
hands, kissing the firm peaks of her breasts, letting
his mouth wander at will over her perfumed skin
until at last he possessed her lips. The dull thud of
the bedroom door as someone closed it jerked
Kelly back to reality, and a deep wave of colour
seared over her as she tried to deny the truth of
Jake's earlier claim that she wanted him.

'Kelly?'

She stiffened as he called her name, hurriedly
stepping out of the shower and reaching for a towel.

'I'm in here,' she called back, her mouth dry with
tension. He could so easily have simply walked in
and found her. And if he had done so would his
experienced eyes have noted the aroused state of
her body—and worse, known the reason for it? It
must be some sort of jet-lag she was suffering from,
she decided muzzily. She had never felt like this
before, not even with Colin. It was completely out
of character for her. Was it? She stiffened, trying to
blot out the tiny voice that mocked acidly that she
had never allowed her own sexual character to
develop. She had killed it at birth, refused to admit
it into her life, and now she was being paid back
with a vengeance.

Outside, she heard sounds of movement and

hurriedly pulled on a robe. 'Don't come in, I won't be a moment!'

She had barely finished speaking when Jake pushed open the door and leaned indolently against the frame.

'I asked you not to come in,' Kelly snapped angrily, trying to tie the sash of her robe. 'Or didn't you hear me?'

'Oh, I heard all right, but you've been around long enough to know that a remark like that is tantamount to asking for the opposite, and so as a mere employee what else could I do but oblige?'

It was the way he said 'mere employee', rather than the words themselves, that underlined the deep cynicism she could see etched alongside his mouth, but surely that couldn't account for the burningly intense anger that turned his eyes from flint to smoke and seemed to rob her of the ability to think or move with her normal efficiency?

'What's the matter?' Jake demanded smokily. 'You don't know what to do when you're confronted by a man who doesn't toe the line—your line—do you, Kelly? You just love calling the shots, don't you? Making men squirm, turning them on and then paying them off, but it won't work with me. So,' he drawled, folding his arms and studying her mockingly, 'if you want me to make love to you, lady, you're damn well going to have to ask this time.'

'Ask?' Kelly was too furious to be careful. 'You're the last man I'd ask for anything and . . . and besides,' she added on a flood of triumph, 'if I wanted a man to make love to me there's always Jeremy!'

'So there is.' His mouth went hard. 'You know, Kelly, I can't quite figure you out. One moment I think you genuinely care about Sue, and really want to protect her from finding out what a creep her husband is, the next I begin to think you're playing some deep game where the prize is Sue's husband with a ring through his nose and that you mean to win him.'

'Think what you like . . . You're here for one reason and one reason only, and that's because I'm paying you, and if you . . .'

'If I forget my place you'll dismiss me? No way. You try it and find out what happens.'

'Meaning you'll tell Sue about Jeremy? If I really did want to break up their marriage I'd let you, wouldn't I?'

'Not necessarily. You see, Kelly, you strike me as the type who likes her life all cut and dried. It wouldn't suit you one little bit to be known as the woman who broke up her friend's marriage and then stole her husband. No, you wouldn't want me telling Sue.'

'You're so sure of yourself . . . so damnably arrogant! Hasn't it occurred to you that you might be wrong?'

'Why should I?' he responded coolly. 'It never occurred to you, did it?'

With that enigmatic remark he started to step past her, his eyes flicking contemptuously over her still damp body as he did so.

'That's something else,' he murmured, smiling with hateful mockery. 'That "still wet from the shower" approach is old hat now—you're going to have to find a new routine—or start paying more.'

Kelly raised her hand automatically, shrinking herself as the sharp sound of it against his lean jaw fractured the silence, leaving a strained dangerous calm during which she watched the white imprint of her hand fade and slowly fill with angry blood until the marks throbbed hotly against the brown skin.

'Oh no, you don't,' Jake muttered thickly as she started to move away. His eyes were the colour of slate, hard and bitter, implacable determination underlining every movement as he placed his palms flat to the wall behind her, imprisoning her against it.

She could feel the heat coming off his body and knew she was trembling.

'Jake, please!' Was that hoarse, panicky voice really hers? She moaned huskily as he lifted one hand and slowly and quite deliberately pulled the pins from her hair until it cascaded on her shoulders. His thumb stroked along her jawline, his fingers forcing her downbent head up until she was forced to meet his eyes, and the murderous rage she saw in their depths told her without the need for any words that this parody of tenderness was a subtle form of punishment, and that he intended that she should never forget how he had repaid her for striking him.

'That's better.' His voice was slurred and Kelly trembled, longing for the strength to be able to push him away and run.

'All it needs is this,' he added, wrenching open her towelling wrap so that the curves of her breasts were exposed, 'and now you look the part completely. There was no need to slap me, though Kelly. Like I said before, all you had to do was ask.'

He bent his head and there was no way she could avoid the insistent stroke of his lips against her own, taunting and tormenting until her lips were parting on a groan, her arms going round his neck, her fingers curling into the thick silky hair at his nape as the torment continued until she couldn't endure it any longer, and she was arching against his body, her mouth clinging pleadingly to his, her small broken murmurs of pleasure filling the thick silence.

'Oh no . . . I'm not going to make it easy for you.'

Her hands were wrenched away, and suddenly she was free, her body aching with unfulfilled need, her mind totally disorientated by the power of the sexual feelings he had aroused.

Appalled, both by the intensity of her desire and the rage she could sense within Jake, she pulled away and darted into the bedroom, dimly registering the closing of the bathroom door behind her.

In the lamplit room her tousled, disordered hair and pale face stared back at her from the mirror. Her lips looked full and swollen, and as she hurriedly dressed in the clean underwear she had laid out Kelly was aware of the swollen fullness of her breasts, her nipples taut beneath the fine silk of her dress. She shivered, unable to believe that the woman staring back at her was her, the reflection was so unfamiliar; not merely because of the different hairstyle and silk dress. It was the more subtle difference that frightened her the most: the darkening of her eyes, almost all pupil, the sleekness of her skin, and the unmistakable softening of every feature. No man looking at her now would ever believe that she was the head of her own company, or that she had kept her emotions in check for years. It was like looking at a stranger, only the stranger was elusively familiar, and Kelly shivered, her tongue nervously touching dry lips. The woman staring back at her—hadn't she seen her before, many years before when she had still been a teenager and Colin and her love for him and had filled her life?

'No!'

Kelly wasn't even aware that she spoke the denial aloud, the sound torn from her throat against muscles tight with despair.

'Kelly, we're leaving in half an hour, are you two nearly ready?'

Sue's voice outside the bedroom door steadied her, turning her to something resembling normality, but her voice shook as she called out a response and ten minutes later her hand still trembled as she carefully tried to apply her eye make-up. Perhaps it was because of that that her eyes seemed darker, more exotic than usual, or perhaps it was simply a trick of the lighting. The slither of silk against her skin was a constant reminder of Jake's hands on her body, and she fought against the memory, brushing her hair with angry strokes and securing it with the pearlised comb.

Sounds of movement from the bathroom had her heading for the door, grabbing her bag as she did so. There was no way she wanted to be in the bedroom when Jake walked into it, neither was there any way she could continue to share the room with him. She didn't care what Sue thought, she decided feverishly, she would have to tell her. Perhaps she could make up some story about not being able to sleep well—she could plead that she didn't want to disturb Jake.

'Oh, Kelly, you look gorgeous—doesn't she, Jeremy?' Sue asked, turning to him for corroboration.

Kelly hated the way Jeremy's eyes moved insultingly over her body in the thin silk.

'Gorgeous,' he agreed softly. 'The ice has melted with a vengeance! I'll have to get Jake to let me into the secret.'

As Sue's genuinely amused laughter filled the room, Kelly wondered how her friend could be so blind to the venom in her husband's eyes. Jeremy still hadn't forgiven her for rejecting him. Men were so vain; so arrogant in their assumption that they had the right to react like spoiled children simply because a woman did not find them desirable.

'Ah, here's Jake—now you'll be able to ask him,' Sue teased Jeremy as Jake strolled into the room.

He had changed into cream pants that clung to the powerfully lean thighs, his cream shirt open at the neck revealing the crisply curling hair that darkened his chest. In comparison to Jake's lithe maleness Jeremy looked flabby and out of condition.

'Ask me what?' Jake prompted, giving Sue a slow smile that appreciated her femininity in her new dress, and watching her friend glow with pleasure. Kelly felt a frisson of emotion she recognised bewilderingly as the beginnings of a knife-sharp pain.

'Oh, just how you managed to turn our ice queen

into a smouldering sex bomb,' Jeremy drawled unpleasantly.

Kelly wondered if anyone else noticed the way she shrank as Jake curled his arm round her waist, drawing her to his side, her nostrils teased by the warm male scent of his body.

'It isn't hard,' Jake told him equably, an excellent facsimile of tenderness softening his gaze as he turned to Kelly and added huskily, 'All you need is love, isn't that right, Kelly?'

She couldn't have moved even if someone had told her a bomb was about to go off next to her. Love! Her pupils dilated with shock, a sickening sensation of anguish filling her. Of course she didn't love Jake. The very idea was ridiculous. How could she? After Colin she knew better than to risk loving any man, least of all one like Jake who made his living from weak, foolish women.

They walked to the villa where the party was being held. Far larger than Sue's father's, its gardens backed on to his, and Sue explained that they owned the land right down to the sea itself, where the owner had a private mooring for his yacht.

The garden itself was illuminated with what seemed to be hundreds of pretty Japanese-style paper lanterns, and as always the absence of the sun seemed to enhance the scent of growing things, so that Kelly's nostrils were full of the scent of wild thyme and other aromatic bushes.

She was lost in a vision of how this island must have appeared to the first Greek adventurers, when Jeremy destroyed her dream by cursing vehemently as he caught his foot in an exposed root.

Kelly winced for her friend as he swore angrily, 'I

suppose it was your bloody stupid idea to walk here,' but to her surprise Jake said coolly, 'Actually it was mine.'

'Huh, I would have thought you'd have had enough of walking after this afternoon. We did the full eighteen holes.'

'Oh, Jeremy dragged you round the full course, did he?' Sue smiled sympathetically at Jake. 'I'm afraid he's something of a golf-aholic, although he tells me he only plays for business reasons. Are you a keen player?'

Kelly's heart turned over as Jake smiled back at Sue, a ridiculous surge of jealousy submerging her in its tormenting depths.

'Not really. I prefer squash.'

'No need to be that modest, old man,' Jeremy cut in acidly. 'He was good enough to beat me.'

Kelly hid a small smile of amusement. Jeremy prided himself on his golf—she had in the past been obliged to listen to him boasting endlessly about his prowess, and it was obvious that he was admitting Jake's superiority with grudging reluctance.

'Oh, we're nearly there—there's the pool,' Sue told them, with evident relief. 'It's full Olympic size—although I've heard that he rarely uses it.'

A short flight of steps brought them on to the same level as the pool and patio area, which was already thronged with other guests. The pool, as Sue had said, was huge, but Kelly doubted that many zealous swimmers would appreciate the design of it, which wasn't rectangular, but instead seemed to form an elongated figure of eight, the smaller circle disappearing inside the house in traditional Hollywood manner.

'That's so that they can use the pool in winter,' Sue informed her knowledgeably. 'Huge glass doors cut off that part of the pool and enclosed it inside. I believe it cost a fortune. And just have a look behind you,' she added, waiting with a knowing grin as Kelly obediently turned and gasped her amazement as she saw what appeared to be a floating white trelliswork gazebo in the centre of the second circle.

'Good heavens,' she managed weakly, while Sue laughed her appreciation. 'Mmm. Vintage Hollywood, isn't it? The third, or was it fourth Mrs Wrayman had the original villa almost torn down and all this done in its place, and just wait until you see the inside. Carne Wrayman is a fanatical collector of Byzantine religious relics and the like. He has some fantastic icons that were brought out of Russia during the Revolution—they're worth a fortune, but then of course he's a millionaire several times over.'

'Sounds just your type,' Jake murmured *sotto voce* against Kelly's hair. 'No worries about him wanting you for your money!'

'Perhaps you've got a point!' Kelly bit out the words, small white teeth snapping together as she fought against her anger.

'Jake darling! How wonderful! What on earth are you doing here?'

A lissom blonde girl extricated herself from the crowd by the pool and almost threw herself into Jake's arms. She was about eighteen, and Kelly knew beyond doubt that the feelings tearing at her with sharply venomous claws were pure feminine jealousy.

'Well, well,' Jeremy murmured tauntingly. 'A little bit of something from his past? You want to watch it, love,' he warned Kelly acidly, 'you might find she's making a takeover bid for the present and the future.'

'Jake, there's someone I want you to meet. Do come with me . . . You won't mind if I borrow him for a minute, will you?' the blonde asked Kelly with an arch smile that revealed surprisingly genuine dimples.

'Feel free.' Her face felt stiff and she knew her smile looked totally unnatural.

'I won't be long,' Jake told her casually before walking away, his arm round the blonde girl's shoulders, her face turned up to his full of laughter, and—Kelly was forced to admit it—love!

'Mmm, I wonder why he was so keen not to introduce her to us.' Jeremy was watching her with a triumph that was unmistakable, and it didn't take a genius to see what he was thinking. Even so, Kelly had to clench her teeth to stop herself retorting when he said with mock concern, 'Perhaps I'd better make a few enquiries. You can't be too careful, you know, Kelly, a woman of your wealth. Okay, I know he has all the trappings of success, but I would hate to see you taken in—again,' he added deliberately.

Kelly went white. The patio seemed to be whirling round, the noise of the party roaring in her ears. Struggling to re-assert her normal control, she managed a husky, 'What do you mean, "again"?'

'Oh, come on, darling!' Jeremy was really enjoying himself now, and Kelly wondered how long he had been storing up this bitterness, this need to

cause her pain and inflict hurt. 'Old Ian told me—
we were at a conference together, we'd had a few
drinks, you know how it is. I happened to mention
you, and he told me about what happened with
Colin, how he deliberately set you up—married
you for your money.'

'Jeremy!' Sue sounded shocked and angry, but
Kelly was past caring. Amazingly, the old story
lacked all the old pain. She couldn't care less what
Jeremy had heard and it no longer caused her the
slightest pang that Colin had not loved her. What
she did feel was regret that she had been foolish
enough to fall for what she could see now had been
a clumsy charm at best, and sorrow that she had let
it spoil so much of her life.

'It's quite all right, Sue,' she managed to say
evenly. 'Jeremy's quite right, Colin did marry me
for my money.'

'But Jake isn't the slightest bit like Colin,' Sue
broke in hotly, 'and I can't think why Jeremy
should suggest that he is. Perhaps it has something
to do with the fact that he beat you at golf,' she
suggested to her husband, who, Kelly was half
amused to see, was regarding her with stupefied
disbelief.

'You ought to apologise to Kelly, Jeremy,' Sue
continued. 'Oh, saved by the bell,' she added.
'Here's our host.'

'Susan, my darling, you grow more lovelier every
time I see you!'

'It's lovely of you to say so, Carne,' Sue responded to the well-built greying man who was
embracing her, 'but we both know you're a liar.'

Carne Wrayman released her to shake Jeremy's

hand and then turned to Kelly, his eyes narrowing in appreciation as he smiled at her.

'You are here alone?' he questioned when Sue had introduced them.

'She is now,' Jeremy responded viciously. 'She's lost her partner to an eighteen-year-old blonde.'

'Is that so?' The hooded eyes studied Kelly again. 'Well then, his loss is my gain. Allow me to escort you to the bar. Sue, you know the way.'

CHAPTER SEVEN

'So, and what do you do with yourself when you're not holidaying on Corfu?' Carne Wrayman asked Kelly.

They were sitting by the patio drinking the driest Martinis Kelly had ever tasted in her life. She had lost sight of Sue and Jeremy, and Jake was just a painful blur on the edge of her vision; someone she tried not to see, just as she tried not to see the blonde girl clinging to his side.

'I . . . I'm in publicity. I have my own company,' Kelly told him briefly.

'A career woman.' Again that sharply hooded glance. 'You know, I find that an incredible turn-on,' Carne Wrayman told her, leaning closer to her, 'and as it happens I'm looking for someone to handle the British side of the publicity for a documentary we're doing. Fancy the idea?'

'I'd have to know more about it,' Kelly told him cautiously. 'You see, we only handle work we feel we can give our best to. I don't believe in making false promises to my clients, and the promises I do make to them I want to be able to fulfil.'

'Baby, I like what I'm hearing,' Carne breathed fervently. 'Something tells me that you and I are going to get along real fine together. Look, why don't we blow—we can go out to my yacht and talk this thing through. We'll get more privacy there. What do you say?'

Kelly's first instinct was to refuse. She glanced across the sea of faces and saw Jake dancing with the blonde girl, her body pressed provocatively close to his, and jealousy burned through her. Like an animal in pain she wanted only to escape, and her eyes were still on the slowly gyrating couple as she murmured distractedly, 'Yes . . . yes . . . fine . . .'

'Good. Good, let's go, then.' Carne Wrayman got up, and Kelly followed him along a path which led down through the gardens, giving the odd tantalising glimpse of the moon-silvered sea and the huge white yacht lit from stem to stern and drifting languidly at anchor.

'Hop in,' Carne instructed, indicating the small powerboat tied up at the jetty. 'The water in this cove is quite deep,' he told her as they headed for the yacht, 'but unfortunately not deep enough for the *Mary Belinda*—after wife number three I got sick of changing her name, and so, although the real Mary Belinda has long since left my life, her namesake remains.'

The small motorboat chugged noisily towards the yacht, Kelly entranced by the reflections of the stars in the midnight-blue water, the swell caused by the boat crested silver by the new moon.

'I've given the crew the night off,' Carne told her as they went on board. He saw Kelly's bemused expression and grinned boyishly. 'Would you like to see over her? She's one of my favourite toys, and I'm idiotically proud of her.'

With good reason, Kelly reflected half an hour later as Carne escorted her into what he described as the 'main saloon'. As large and lavishly equipped

as a small drawing-room, the room was decorated
in soft shades of green and toning cream.

'It's . . . it's like something out of a film,' she
managed at last. 'A floating stately home!'

Carne laughed. 'You should see some of the
yachts that put in to Corfu, they make mine look
very small beer indeed—but I still haven't shown
you my own private quarters.'

Still smiling, Kelly followed him through a door
and into a corridor carpeted in a thick pale cream
carpet.

As Carne opened a door she caught a glimpse of
the room beyond it; almost stark in contrast to the
pastel prettiness of the 'saloon', it was furnished in
a richly Oriental style with a low bed, and several
items of beautifully lacquer-worked furniture, including an antique 'medicine cabinet' and a screen.
The walls were painted a vivid scarlet, the bed
covered in black silk.

'Very sybaritic,' she murmured to Carne, 'and
quite different from the rest of the décor.'

'Yes, I had my own suite redecorated when I
divorced my third wife. Do you like it?'

A tiny frisson of warning prickled along her
spine. There was a look in Carne's eyes that she
recognised and distrusted.

'It's . . . it's very eye-catching,' she told him,
edging back towards the door. 'But hardly the place
to discuss business.'

'That depends,' Carne told her, watching her
intently. 'On the business, and the potential business partners. I could put a good deal of work your
way, Kelly . . .'

'Provided, in return?' she questioned evenly.

She was furiously angry, not so much with Carne as with herself by being stupid enough to get herself in this situation. Good heavens, how many times in the past had she been faced with the same potential hazard? More than she cared to remember, but this was the first time she had been idiotic enough to walk blindly into the trap as naïvely as a child.

'My dear,' Carne protested, 'need we be so crude? You aren't doing much for my ego, you know.'

'I shouldn't think it's in much danger from anything I can do,' Kelly said drily. 'I'm not stupid enough to believe you have any interest in me as a person, Carne. This is simply an exercise in power politics.'

'How astute you are!' He drawled the words pleasantly enough, but there was a look in his eyes that warned Kelly that he was annoyed. 'I thought you and I were two of a kind.'

'Perhaps it would be as well if I left . . .'

'From whose point of view?' There was no humour in his smile now. 'If you return to the villa now, having been seen leaving in my company, my guests, and even worse the inevitable press photographer who always manages to gatecrash these do's, will jump to the correct, and as far as I'm concerned, humiliating conclusions. I don't want you making a fool out of me by going back to the villa now, Kelly. You're a grown woman, you knew what you were doing when you agreed to come here with me. Okay, now you've changed your mind, but I haven't changed mine.'

He lunged for her, taking Kelly off guard as he grasped her arm. Pain jerked up her arm as he dragged her towards him. The urbane host who had amused and entertained her was gone. In his place was a man governed by vanity and obsessed with his public image, and she had been a fool not to read the truth in the weak mouth and greedy eyes before.

Common sense warned her against panicking; that was just exactly what he hoped she would do. Cool cynicism would be a far more effective weapon if she could just keep her head long enough to use it.

'Look,' she pleaded, playing for time, 'I can understand why you're annoyed—and some of the blame does lie with me. I wasn't thinking properly and I genuinely thought you did want to talk business. Let's go back to the villa together—that should stop any gossip, and I give you my word as far as I'm concerned that will be the end of the whole thing . . .'

'Your word!' He laughed harshly. 'My God, if there's one thing I've learned over the years it's that when a woman gives you her "word", it means exactly nothing. And besides,' he said softly, 'I want you. You're a very desirable woman—my kind of woman.'

'But you aren't my kind of man,' Kelly retorted pointedly. 'And now—I'm leaving, with or without you.'

'Brave words,' Carne sneered, 'but unfortunately for you no more than that. You can't start the boat without the ignition key, which I have here.' He patted his pocket. 'And besides, you couldn't outrun me, Kelly, but go ahead if you want to.'

His voice told her that he would love her to try

and make a run for it; that he would enjoy her panic and fear, and even though inwardly she was tense with anxiety and dread, Kelly forced herself to stand her ground and say calmly, 'I have no intention to staying here with you, Carne—or of allowing you to make love to me.'

His sneer almost made her panic.

'How are you going to stop me?' he mocked, tightening his grip on her arm. 'And don't start telling me you'll cry "rape", Kelly. The courts are getting tired of trumped-up charges from women who change their minds at the last minute.'

White-faced and thoroughly frightened, Kelly was forced to admit the truth of his comment. Even if she were to accuse him of rape she doubted that her case would stand much chance of success in court. By her own folly she had placed herself in a vulnerable position. She had come willingly with Carne to his boat, after all.

As though he read her mind and sensed victory, Carne pulled her towards him, triumph flaring in his eyes.

'Admit it, Kelly,' he breathed, nauseating her with his self-conceit, his wine-fumed breath reminding her that he had probably had a considerable amount to drink,

This was confirmed as he raised his free hand and started to fumble clumsily with the straps of her dress, and although what he had had to drink didn't appear to have affected his strength—he was still holding her arm in a bruising grip—it did seem to have affected his co-ordination.

A miasma of panic settled round her like a mind-paralysing cloud as she tried to fight free of him, her body tensing automatically against the intrusion of his hands against her skin, anger giving way to stark terror and the age-old human instinct to fight for survival.

'Hellcat!' Carne swore thickly at one point as Kelly scratched frantically at his face, his hand going automatically to the long red welts she had drawn along his skin. Momentarily free, Kelly reacted, instantly, racing for the open door, finding her way almost by blind instinct up the nearest companionway, lungs bursting, heart pounding with the fear that fuelled her flight. On the deck her flight was suddenly impeded by a solid mass that crushed the breath out of her body, the bite of strong fingers on her shoulders making her shudder with panic and despair.

'Kelly . . . Kelly . . . What the hell's going on?'

'Jake?' She stared at him in utter disbelief, suddenly galvanised into action as she heard Carne swearing and breathing heavily down below.

Jake registered her panic and smiled cynically.

'What's the matter? Did lover boy prove too much for you?'

'He told me he wanted to talk about business,' Kelly muttered, feeling foolish and very much on the defensive.

'And you're trying to tell me you fell for it?'

Kelly flinched as she heard angry footsteps on the companionway, clutching instinctively at Jake's arm, her eyes widening with fear.

'Oh, please, let's go!'

Carne had gained the deck and stood there, swaying slightly, his face livid with rage.

'Just who the hell are you?' he demanded thickly, advancing on Jake.

'I'm a friend of Kelly's,' Jake replied evenly. 'Thank the kind man for his hospitality, Kelly,' he drawled mockingly. 'It's time we left.'

For a moment, Kelly thought Carne was going to hurl himself at Jake and she held her breath, terrified by the thought of more violence. But half a dozen feet short of Jake Carne came to an uncertain standstill.

'Get her out of my sight,' he muttered angrily. 'Frigid little bitch, I didn't really want her anyway!'

All the way back in the boat the words reverberated endlessly through her mind, an acid refrain that seemed to burn through her frail protection, reminding her achingly of Colin and the taunts he had thrown at her, destroying the frail self-possession she had built up in the years between and leaving her as vulnerable to his rejection as she had been then.

She was shivering by the time Jake stopped the motorboat, barely aware of him standing up to throw anchor over the side.

'Come on, jump out, you'll have to wade the rest of the way.'

She shivered, backing away from him instinctively as he reached out his hand. The boat rocked wildly. Kelly heard Jake curse and then she was overbalancing, falling backwards into the cold dark water, her startled cry of protest choked off by the seawater filling her mouth and nostrils.

Her panic subsided almost instantly as her feet touched the sandy bottom, and by the time Jake reached her she had regained her balance. The cold

water had the effect of shocking her back into an
awareness of the present; of Jake's angrily icy face,
and the bedraggled picture she must present in her
seawater-doused hair and soaking dress. Why had
Jake come to look for her and, more important,
how had he known where to look?

'Sue was concerned about you,' he told her,
obviously reading her mind. 'She couldn't find you,
and she seemed to think you might be . . . upset,
for some reason.'

Kelly was glad of the darkness as her face flamed.
Sue meant that she had thought she would be
jealous because Jake had disappeared with the
blonde.

'That doesn't explain how you knew where to
find me,' she retorted coolly, dragging the rags of
her composure around her, retreating into the protection of the cold hauteur that had worked so well
in the past.

'You were seen leaving with Wrayman,' Jake
told her tersely, as he waded on to the beach and
turned to help her. The moonlight fell sharply on
his face and for a second his features seemed to
tense, a muscle beating violently in his jaw. He
looked angry, and more . . .

'Kelly, come on. We're both soaked through.
We can't stand here all night. I take it you don't
want to go back to the party?'

'Meaning you do? I'm perfectly capable of returning to the villa on my own,' she told him acidly,
'so if you want to return to your girl-friend . . .'

'My girl-friend?' He frowned, and then his expression changed, a mocking smile playing round
his mouth. 'Ah yes, of course. But, Kelly, you are

forgetting something. You are my girl-friend—at least, you are while I am still in your employ.'

For some reason she wanted to cry. She felt the tears sting the back of her eyes and knew with detached certainty that this was only the beginning of the pain she was going to experience. Where and why it had happened she didn't know, but she had fallen in love with Jake.

In a daze she followed him up the beach, barely aware of the fact that he had turned to wait for her, until she felt the warm clasp of his hand on hers.

'Cold?'

She nodded, wondering if she was hallucinating and imagining the tenderness in the word.

The night air was quite warm, but the sea and the shocks she had sustained had left her chilled to the marrow. By the time they reached the garden of Sue's father's villa she was shivering so much that her teeth were chattering. Jake, although equally wet, seemed impervious to the cold.

'Come into the sitting-room and I'll pour you a stiff drink,' he suggested curtly as they entered the house. 'It will help combat the shock.'

'No!' Kelly didn't want to tell him that she always associated the sort of drink he meant with the one the police constable had given her when he broke the news about Colin.

'I'll go and have a shower. I'm just cold, that's all.'

Jake shrugged, the powerful shoulders damply encased in the thin silk shirt, his jeans clinging to his body in a way that made her senses respond over-poweringly to the masculinity of him.

The shower helped, but she couldn't banish the

ice-cold knot of sickness lodged inside her heart.
Carne's final words had left a barb that festered
powerfully, no matter how she tried to blot them
out, and this, coupled with the knowledge of her
love for Jake, left her feeling totally disorientated
and achingly vulnerable.

She longed to go to bed and sleep so that she
could blot out what had happened—forget everything, but she knew that sleep would be impossible,
and then she remembered Sue saying that she had
some sleeping tablets her doctor had prescribed.
Ordinarily, Kelly wouldn't have dreamed of taking
medicine prescribed for someone else, but tonight
she couldn't endure to lie knowing that Jake was
either lying in the opposite bed or, more likely,
sharing the bed of the blonde girl who had made her
admiration of him all so plain.

She was heading for Sue's bathroom when the
living-room door opened and Jake emerged.

He frowned when he saw her, and Kelly was
absurdly aware of the brief towel she had wrapped
around her body—and the insulting remarks Jake
had made earlier. Her face burned as he looked at
her. Did he think she had done this purely to attract
his attention?

'I wanted to borrow a couple of Sue's sleeping
pills,' she muttered jerkily. 'I'm sure she won't
mind, and I . . .'

'Want to forget what happened on board the
yacht, is that it? What did happen, by the way?
Were you genuinely running from Wrayman or
were you simply egging him on?'

A sudden rush of tears to her eyes blinded her
momentarily, and she smothered a tiny, betraying

protest, turning swiftly on her heel. It was too dangerous to risk bandying words with Jake feeling the way she did at the moment—she could only lose.

'Kelly!'

It seemed he wasn't content with reducing her to tears. His fingers grasped her arm, spinning her round so hard that she gasped, fingers clutching nervously at her towel as it slipped precariously low over her breasts.

'Do these mean that it was genuine?' Jake demanded softly, his fingers oddly gentle as they brushed the dampness from her cheeks.

She tried to speak, to tell him coldly that if she was crying it was simply reaction, but instead, to her horror, the tears flowed even faster, like a dam bursting, falling harder as she struggled to suppress them and the emotions storming through her.

'Kelly!'

Jake spoke her name with unmistakable urgency.

'I know—you hate seeing women cry,' she tried to joke—but suddenly it wasn't a joke any longer as Jake smothered a curse, pulling her savagely into his arms as he muttered hoarsely, 'I hate seeing *you* cry. God, if Wrayman had hurt you . . .'

'It was my own fault. I should never have gone with him. God knows I've spent enough time avoiding similar situations, but tonight . . .'

Within the circle of Jake's arms, she shrugged, realising in amazement how easily she had confided in him.

'Would you like me to stay with you—until you fall asleep?'

Oh, she was tempted!

'Let's start again, Kelly,' Jake was murmuring softly. 'Somehow we got off on the wrong foot and we've stayed that way ever since, apart from one or two illuminating incidents. I could have killed Wrayman when he walked off with you tonight.'

'You saw us?' Kelly was astonished, and raised her head to look at him.

He grimaced slightly, his eyes darkening as they probed the shadowy swell of her breasts where her towel had slipped.

'I saw you,' he confirmed. 'I thought you were doing it to annoy me.'

When she looked puzzled, he said softly, 'Oh, come on, Kelly, you know how much I want you, you aren't blind—but then, of course, I'm not keeping to my place if I want you, am I? I'm only the hired help.'

'Jake?'

Her voice was wondering, hesitantly hopeful. Jake wanted her. She searched his face distractedly for signs that he was lying, but there were none. She could see the sharp hunger in his eyes, echoed in the tautness of his body against hers, as he held her.

'Don't play with *me*, Kelly,' he warned her, his voice rough with emotion. 'Let's have no misunderstandings this time. I want you, and . . .'

'And I want you, Jake,' Kelly told him huskily, her fingers trembling as she touched his face, trying to reassure herself that he was real, 'but first there's something I have to tell you.'

She wanted to tell him about Colin, about why she had been so bitterly suspicious of him. It didn't matter that he had no money, or how he earned his

living, she decided passionately. What mattered
was the way they felt about one another. He
wanted her, and every feminine instinct she
possessed told her that she would be a fool if she
turned her back on this chance of happiness simply
because of pride and money. What did it matter if
she was rich and he was poor? What did it matter
what anyone else thought? What did anything matter except for this wonderful, glorious happiness
bubbling up inside her?

'Later, Kelly,' Jake was saying roughly, 'tell me
about it later. Right now—right now . . .' he added
huskily, 'I can think of better ways of communicat-
ing than simply by the spoken word.'

He lifted her in his arms and Kelly clung to
the breadth of his shoulders, her heart pounding
shakily as he pushed open the door to their room.

She was still in his arms when Jake bent his head
to kiss her, her lips parting eagerly beneath his, her
body trembling with heated urgency as he gradually
slid her to her feet, every contour of her moulded
against him so that she could almost feel his pulse
beat.

'Kelly.'

She let him unfasten her towel, her own fingers
making eager inroads into the buttons on his shirt,
peeling it back, her eyes mesmerised by the sight of
his body. His hands cupped her breasts and they
swelled instantly to his touch. Her skin felt as
though it were on fire with a burningly dry heat, the
frenzied kisses she pressed against Jake's throat
and shoulders eliciting a husky imprecation and the
fierce assault of his mouth against her skin, his
hands moving hungrily over her body, touching and

exploring, bringing her to a fever pitch of sexual excitement.

Kelly was completely lost in the storm of sensual pleasure Jake evoked, stroking his torso feverishly as he savaged her mouth in explicit demand, releasing her lips to mutter hoarsely, 'For God's sake, Kelly, what are you doing to me?'

And then he was lifting her in his arms, and striding towards the bed, lowering his head to capture one taut nipple with his lips before he released her, savouring its burgeoning sweetness until Kelly sobbed out loud with pleasure, her stomach muscles cramping excitingly, her body throbbing tormentingly as Jake lowered her on to the bed.

She shivered for a moment as the coolness of the night air struck her skin, and then Jake was beside her, covering her trembling flesh with the warmth of his, and the feel of him against her was nothing like the humiliation she had known with Colin.

It was easy to give herself up to the seduction of his touch, to respond with caresses of her own, taking fierce delight from the harsh sounds of pleasure her fingers drew from his throat, and the kisses that followed them.

When his hand stroked along her inner thigh she tensed, nightmare memories flooding back, but her desire and love for Jake were more powerful than her fear, and intense waves of pleasure followed her initial fear, her body arching; wanting and inciting with age-old instinct the union of their flesh.

In the darkness she heard the ragged, charged quality of Jake's breathing, and felt the perspiration beading his skin as he muttered hoarsely beneath his breath, cupping her face and stroking her lips with his, until she clung mindlessly, exulting in the fierce thrust of his body and the savage passion of his kiss.

Somewhere, dimly in the recesses of her mind, she was registering pain, but she didn't care; she wanted this pain, wanted the fierce maleness of Jake with a need that overrode everything else, and when he tensed, withdrawing from her, she was plunged into a pit of bitter rejection, cringing away from him as he snapped on the bedside lamp.

'Kelly, look at me.'

She quivered under the harshness of his tone.

'Kelly . . .'

'No! Please, I . . .' To her horror she started to cry, not silent tears, but tearing sobs that shook her body and made her throat ache.

'Kelly, for God's sake!' She shrank beneath the whiplash of anger, shivering with self-loathing and humiliation. 'Why didn't you tell me?'

It was pointless and undignified trying to pretend she didn't understand.

'I tried to,' she managed wearily, 'but you wouldn't listen.'

'Are you going to tell me about it?'

'What do you want to hear?' Her voice sounded bitter and sour, but she couldn't help it, couldn't rid herself of the taste of rejection. 'Would you like to hear how my husband only married me for my money; how he tried to rape me on our wedding night, but how he couldn't bring himself to possess me in the end—he didn't really want me, you see, he only wanted my money, and making love to me was a price he found in the end he simply couldn't pay. So he left me and went to his girl-friend, only he was killed on the way. Funny, isn't it really . . .'

She started to laugh, a high bitter sound that went on and on, until Jake shook her roughly and then smothered the sound with his lips, kissing her until she was fighting for breath; fighting for the control to reject him as he had rejected her.

'You don't have to make love to me,' she told him when she finally managed to pull away. 'I'll still pay you.'

'I damn well ought to thrash you for that!' Jake ground out, and in the darkness she caught the burn of anger in his eyes, 'and besides, you're wrong. I do have to make love to you.' He said it so quietly that at first she thought she had misheard, but then he added slowly, as though he wanted every single word to sink in:

'I'm sorry for what happened with Colin and it explains a great deal I couldn't understand before—but, Kelly, I'm not Colin, and you can't spend the rest of your life punishing yourself because one man didn't want you. I want you,' he said quietly, 'and the only reason we aren't already lovers is simply that it threw me to realise that you were still a virgin.'

'Meaning that you'd prefer me to have more experience,' Kelly said bitterly. 'I'm sorry if I don't come up to your undoubtedly high standards, but . . .'

The crudity of the expression he used shocked her into silence. She stared across at him in the darkness, wondering if she was being a fool, but her body still ached for him, and she still loved him.

'Virginity is more a state of mind than an actual
physical reality—at least that's my view, and my
strongest feeling at the moment is one of pity—oh,
not for you,' he said tersely, 'for Colin, for being
fool enough to turn his back on you. No, I tell a lie,'
he added drily. 'If I'm honest, my *strongest* feeling
right now is my desire for you, but I don't intend to
force any issues, Kelly. I want you—and badly, but
I want you to want me too. I want you to experience
pleasure in my arms, not simply give me pleasure.
Do you understand what I'm trying to say?'

Her mouth had gone dry. Jake was being unfair,
forcing her to make the decision, and yet inwardly
she acknowledged that he was right; that it was her
decision, and the fact that he had the strength to
allow her to make it only increased her love for
him.

'I . . . I want you, Jake.'

They were the hardest words she had ever had to
utter, and for one terrifying moment when he made
no response she thought it had all been a trick, a
trap, and panic welled up inside her, fear crawling
along her spine.

'Oh God, Kelly, I thought you were never going
to be able to say it!'

She didn't know who moved first, but suddenly
she was in his arms, his lips touching her hair,
kissing the dampness from her cheeks, his thumb
stroking the quivering fullness of her lips, and she
knew joyously, overwhelmingly, that everything
was going to be all right.

CHAPTER EIGHT

TOWARDS dawn, Kelly surfaced briefly. The comforting weight of Jake's arm lay across her ribs, securing her against him. Her body felt lethargic, totally relaxed, as bonelessly sensual as a small cat's, and she smiled secretly, remembering Jake's lovemaking and her own abandoned response to it. Jake moved, eyes still closed, nuzzling her throat, drawing her down against him, her body instantly pliant and responsive, as though it remembered the pleasure they had shared earlier.

The next time she woke up Kelly was alone. She padded across to the bathroom, recognising the faint tang of Jake's soap and cologne, and wondering why he had not woken her. Today they would have to talk. She loved him, and she wasn't going to let her chance of happiness slip away from her through pride. What good was her wealth if it separated her from the only thing that she really wanted—Jake's love? Did he love her? Kelly didn't know, but she wanted him to know that she was willing to share equally with him all her worldly goods. The sexes were equal nowadays, she reminded herself bracingly, she had always fought to be considered the equal of her male colleagues, and surely she wasn't hypocritical enough to want to revert to the typical male/female superior/inferior status now? What did it matter if they lived on her money? What did it matter if Jake had no career or

profession to follow? Banishing all her niggling
doubts, she showered quickly, marvelling at the
difference a handful of hours could make. Even her
flesh felt different—softer, more responsive, glow-
ing with a soft radiance that was reflected in her
face. But where was Jake?

She found Sue and Jeremy breakfasting on the
patio, tension hanging almost visibly on the air.

'Morning, Kelly, did you enjoy the party?' Sue
enquired in an over-bright, forced voice.

'How could she enjoy it? She didn't spend a good
deal of time at the party, did she? Two millionaires
in one night—that's pretty good going by anyone's
standards, never mind a woman who's been fooling
the world for years that she's as frigid as an
iceberg!'

'Jeremy!'

'Two millionaires!'

Sue and Kelly spoke together, Jeremy ignoring
his wife to turn and smirk at Kelly, 'You mean you
didn't know?'

'Know what?' Kelly demanded. The phone
started to ring and Sue got up hurriedly. 'It might
be Dad,' she explained, 'he said he might ring. By
the way, Kelly, Jake said to tell you he's just gone
into town and that he won't be long.'

She got up and left, ignoring her husband, and
Kelly wondered if the two of them had quarrelled
during the party.

'So you didn't know, then?' Jeremy continued
when Sue had gone. 'I thought not. Fooled you
nicely, didn't he? That blonde girl he was with at
the party knew all right . . .'

A cold tight feeling was gripping her.

'Know what, Jeremy?' she asked tautly.

'That Jake is a millionaire. She obviously recognised him straight away, and I made a few discreet enquiries at the party. It seems your Jake has extensive interests ranging almost worldwide, although he normally keeps a low profile. I bet he though it was hilarious when you walked into that agency and mistook him for one of the staff!'

She must not faint, Kelly told herself grimly. She must not give way in front of Jeremy, watching her, waiting to gloat over her.

'He told you about that?' she managed in a carefully controlled voice, while the icy cold invading her body almost burned in its intensity. She was shaking inwardly, but she daren't let Jeremy see it.

'How else would I know about it? He must have laughed his socks off afterwards! You hired him to keep me at bay, didn't you?

'Well, the joke's on you, Kelly,' Jeremy told her savagely, 'and how! You've fallen for him, haven't you? Let him inside your precious defences; let him make love to you, and all the time he was laughing at you—making a fool of you!'

It couldn't be true! Sickness boiled up inside her. It couldn't be true. Jake a millionaire. Jake deliberately deceiving her, encouraging her to fall in love with him. And yet Jeremy couldn't have made up something like that! But why had Jake confided in Jeremy?

'How does it feel to be a loser, clever lady?' Jeremy taunted. 'You should have stayed within your own league, Kelly. He'll be dining out on the story of how he fooled you for months. I wouldn't be surprised if he didn't deliberately encourage you

to fall in love with him. Quite an amusing diversion
for a man like him, especially with a woman like
you, who wouldn't normally let a man of his type
within a hundred miles of her.'

Kelly wanted to blot out the taunting words;
words she knew were all too painfully true. Like a
film played jerkily backwards she relived those
moments when she had first walked into the
agency; Jake's surprise at seeing her; the feeling
she had had on several occasions that his manner
was not in accord with his subservient role. Dear
God, why had he done it?

She cringed to remember how she had revealed
her innermost thoughts and feelings to him; how
she had told him about Colin, and then trembled
trustingly in his arms as he brought her to full
womanhood, glorying in her joyous response to his
lovemaking when it reached its peak of fierce intensity.

The vulnerable core of her ached for her foolish-
ness. Hadn't she learned her lesson the first time
with Colin? Why couldn't she be like other women
she knew, content to take sexual pleasure where
she found it, without experiencing the need to
involve her heart and mind as well? She had loved
Jake; had been prepared to share with him everything she owned, while he . . .

'You'd have been better off with me,' Jeremy
repeated.

'Except that you happen to be married to Sue,'
Kelly reminded him coldly, turning swiftly on her
heel.

As she walked into the villa Sue was just emerging, looking tired and pale.

'Kelly?'

'I'm leaving, Sue,' Kelly told her shortly, 'I'm flying back to London on the first available flight.' Her mouth twisted bitterly.

'But what about Jake?'

Kelly laughed harshly, 'What about him?'

'Oh, Kelly, if you've quarrelled, I'm sure you'll make it up again. Why don't you wait until he comes back from town?'

'No.' Kelly was icily firm outwardly, but inwardly she was an aching mass of pain and confusion, still half unable to believe what was happening to her.

Less than an hour later she was on her way to the airport, her final goodbyes to Sue and Jeremy, brief and hurried.

She was lucky enough to get a cancellation on a flight leaving for London within the hour, and as she waited in the departure lounge Kelly tried not to think about what had happened. Was it really only last night she had lain in Jake's arms, feeling that at last she had come home?

Fool, fool, she chided herself bitterly. She ought to have known better. She of all people ought to have known. How Jeremy must have enjoyed learning the truth! When and why had Jake deliberately decided to deceive her, or had it simply been an impulse decision which had snowballed to the point where he had conceived the idea of making her fall in love with him?

Her flight was called, and she walked towards the terminal automatically, freezing as she recognised the blonde girl from the party. Today she was dressed casually in jeans and a tee-shirt, but there was no mistaking that blonde hair or those perfectly classical features.

And she wasn't alone. Kelly's heart jerked, ungainly as a puppet as she recognised the back of Jake's dark head, inclined now towards his companion. Even as Kelly watched, the blonde girl raised herself on tiptoe, flinging her arm round Jake's neck and kissing him enthusiastically.

Hot tears of jealousy scorched her eyes and, pain a living, tormenting thing inside her.

After a lifetime of agony in case Jake saw her, and witnessed her jealousy, she was safely on the plane and they were taking off. Fortunately, the blonde girl was nowhere to be seen. What had Jake told Sue to tell her? That he had gone to town? But he hadn't said anything about the reason for his visit, such as the fact that he was seeing his girlfriend off at the airport—but then there was so much he hadn't told her, and last night when those husky, passionate words of need had seared and melted her skin wherever his mouth touched, he had said nothing of love, nothing of the truth, while she, poor crazy fool that she was, had told him with every gesture and embrace that she was wholly and irrevocably besotted with him. She had thought the exquisite pleasure they had shared had been something unique to them. A dull flush of colour suffused her skin, and she writhed mentally, wondering if Jake would tell his girl-friend about what had happened; possibly laugh and joke about it; about *her* and the insecurities she had revealed all too plainly to him in the moments before the final throes of passion had swept aside restraint and selfconsciousness.

She cringed inwardly, huddling down into her seat, taking refuge behind a magazine, trying to convince herself that she was merely the victim of a bad dream; that when she returned to London she would wake up to find that Jake had never really existed.

'Kelly, have you seen this?'

Kelly frowned as her assistant thrust a letter under her nose, her manner one of contained excitement.

'What is it?' Kelly asked her, glancing at the letter, and stiffening a little as she did so.

'Isn't it fantastic?' Maisie demanded. 'I never dreamed we'd be invited to tender for a contract like this! Carew's is a huge multi-national organisation. I've always thought they were based in the States.'

'Mmm.' Kelly was nearly as impressed as her assistant, but since her return from Corfu she had found it difficult to throw herself as completely into her work. 'It seems that the chairman wants to meet me for preliminary discussions.' She frowned. 'I wonder why they chose us?'

'It could be something to do with that article they ran on us in that Sunday supplement,' Maisie suggested.

The article in question had appeared in one of the upmarket Sundays several weeks ago, and Kelly eyed her thoughtfully.

'Could be,' she conceded at last, 'although I shouldn't have thought the chairman of a multi-national like Carew's would be impressed by some-

thing he read in a colour supplement. I think I'll
have a word with Ian. I'm a bit wary of this one. We
could too easily find ourselves involved in heavy
preliminary expenses without anything to show for
it in the end. Including us in the tender might just
be a sop to some eccentric on the Board. Multi-
nationals normally run with their own kind, and
that being the case, why aren't they using one of the
large American companies?'

Two hours later she was putting the same question to Ian over lunch at the Ritz.

'Kelly, you're getting far too suspicious,' Ian
laughed when she had finished. 'Hasn't anyone
ever warned you about refusing gifts from the
gods? And that's what this contract could be. I
don't have to remind you about what the recession
is doing to your particular industry. Oh, I know
you've plenty of work in hand for the next few
months—but after that?'

Kelly knew he was speaking the truth, but why
would Carew's approach her? She was very small
fry indeed by their standards.

'It says in the letter they want me to fly to
Edinburgh. The company has offices up there.'

'They've got considerable interests in oil, Edinburgh is closer to the Scottish oilfields than London. Why are you such a doubting Thomas?' Ian
teased her. 'This could be a tremendous opportunity for the company. I don't know what's happened
to you recently. You've changed.'

'I'm getting older,' Kelly pointed out wryly. She
knew she had changed, and why she wasn't as
singleminded about the company as she had previously been, but despite the speculation in Ian's

eyes, she wasn't going to enlighten him. That was a private pain; a deep and bitter ache that couldn't be assuaged by discussion with someone else.

'Oh yeah?' Ian's voice was openly derisive. 'You're a very beautiful woman, Kelly. I've always thought so, but recently there's been—oh, I don't know, a softening; a more womanly look about you.'

'We're here to talk about Carew's,' Kelly reminded him crisply, 'and there's no need to flirt with me, Ian. You're in no danger of losing the company's business.'

His hurt expression made her feel ashamed of her outburst, but because she couldn't explain to him that it had been to protect herself that she had snapped at him, Kelly said nothing, simply directing several questions to him about the Carew Organisation.

In response, she didn't learn much more than she knew already; namely that Carew's were very big in the petro-chemical world; that they had subsidiaries all over the world and that the chairman was an elusive, almost secretive man about whom very little was known.

'He's English, oddly enough,' Ian told her. '"R.J.", I believe his American colleagues call him, although in actual fact he's . . .'

'Sir Richard Carew,' Kelly supplemented for him. 'Yes, I've been reading up on him too, but I couldn't find out very much, apart from the fact that he built the company up practically from nothing.'

'Well, from very modest beginnings,' Ian agreed. 'When he came down from Cambridge he inherited a small company on the Clyde involved in re-fitting ships.'

'Mmm . . . There's something of a myth about the company's success, isn't there?' Kelly mused.

'More, a case of being in the right place at the right time and plenty of luck, coupled with a good deal of hard work, but I agree, it does make good reading. And you're to meet Carew himself, are you? You're very honoured, I hope you realise. He still insists on running them himself, although they say his son will soon be taking over. He's the one who engineered the company's success in the petro-chemical field.'

A week later, Kelly flew from Heathrow to Edinburgh, stomach clenching nervously as the shuttle flight came in to land.

A chauffeur-driven car collected her from the airport, the driver polite but withdrawn as he negotiated the Edinburgh traffic.

The Carew building was a large imposing one, and Kelly suppressed a flutter of nervousness as the car came to a halt. A receptionist smiled warmly at her as she entered the foyer, indicating that she take a seat, while she pressed some buttons on her telephone and spoke quietly into the receiver.

'If you'd just like to take the lift to the tenth floor Sir Richard's secretary will be waiting for you,' the girl told Kelly with another smile.

There was a mirror in the lift and Kelly couldn't resist checking her appearance swiftly in it. She *had* changed since her return from Corfu. For one thing, she had had her hair cut—not short, but in a softly curving bell that suited her classical features, and the suit she was wearing was in soft muted pinks, far more shapely and feminine than the clothes she had previously worn. She had told herself that she wouldn't allow what had happened between Jake and herself to affect her at all, but somehow she had found herself spurning the clothes she had once favoured, her eyes drawn almost hypnotically to softer shades, more feminine styles. Deep down inside her she knew that Jake was responsible for this resurgence of femininity, but she hated having to admit it even to herself.

The lift stopped and the doors opened. Kelly stepped into a starkly elegant foyer decorated in shades of blue and grey.

A door opened and an immaculately dressed girl came towards her.

'Sir Richard will be with you in a second,' she told Kelly. 'Would you care for a cup of coffee while you're waiting?'

Too nervous to really want a drink, Kelly nevertheless accepted. What on earth was the matter with her? She had never felt like this before; but then they had never been invited to tender for such an important contract, and she was conscious of the tension building up inside her as the girl disappeared and a heavy, almost oppressive silence closed over the foyer.

A door opened, making Kelly jump, despite the fact that she had been waiting for it. The man who came towards her was dressed in a formal business suit, dark grey with a thin chalk stripe, a silk shirt and a toning striped tie, his dark hair curling against his collar, the expensive styling of his jacket doing

nothing to minimise the power of the body it con-
cealed.

Her heart in her mouth, Kelly watched almost
mesmerised, her strangled 'Jake!!!' seeming to
echo drily around the room as she struggled to her
feet and stared at Jake in appalled disbelief.

'You seem surprised.'

He drawled the words casually, bending his dark
head to remove a minute scrap of fluff from his
sleeve, while Kelly's mind whirled, stupidly. What
was Jake doing here?

'I don't know what you're doing here Jake, but I
can't talk to you now,' she managed at last, fighting
for composure. 'I have an appointment with Sir
Richard to . . .'

'To discuss some PR work for the company?'
Jake interposed smoothly. 'Yes, I know, and my
father has asked me to handle it for him. He
has been called away unavoidably—the Energy
Minister.'

'Your father?' Kelly almost whispered the
words. 'Your father is . . .'

'Sir Richard Carew? Yes, that's right. I'm Jake
Fielding Carew. Ah, here's Helen with your coffee.
Mrs Langdon will have her coffee in my room,
Helen, and you can bring a cup for me as well if you
will.'

Listening to the crisply authoritative tones, Kelly
knew that she wasn't, as she had first thought,
simply hallucinating.

Jake took her arm, steering her firmly towards
the door he had just opened. His office was less
austere than the foyer, but still very functional.
Kelly, attuned to such nuances, could tell by the

way Helen brought his coffee that the secretary not only admired him as a man, she also very evidently respected him. Kelly felt stunned, unable to take in what was happening.

'Look, what's going on?' she demanded angrily. 'I was told that Sir Richard wanted to see me.'

'And so he did,' Jake agreed smoothly, 'but, as I explained, something came up and he asked me to talk to you instead. How much do you know about Carew's?' he asked, watching her with eyes suddenly metallic and hard. 'Or were you simply hoping to charm my father into giving you a contract? You'll find me a much tougher proposition, Kelly.'

'Oh, I'm sure of it,' Kelly agreed bitterly, on the point of storming out of the room, but something kept her in her seat. Some deep-seated aching need to remain where she was simply drinking in Jake's familiar features, her heart pounding mercilessly as she remembered the heavy thud of it against her own; the lean, tanned hands now resting distantly on the blotter, caressing her, drawing from her a tumultuous response.

Her mouth tightened and she looked across the desk. 'How can you sit there and accuse me . . . When you deliberately deceived me, deliberately let me think that . . .'

'That I was available for hire?' Jake mocked, an acid smile twisting his mouth. 'Believe me, Kelly, you can't regret it anything like as much as I do.'

'I don't think there's any point in continuing this discussion,' Kelly said unsteadily, reaching for her bag. 'I can't pretend to understand why you've gone to these elaborate lengths to arrange this meeting, Jake—I am right in presuming you did arrange it, I suppose?' When he didn't answer, she rushed on, 'I'm surprised you had the audacity to arrange it after . . .'

'So am I,' Jake agreed curtly, cutting across her furious words, 'but nevertheless I did.'

'Haven't you already done enough?' Kelly choked, terrified by the feeling of her emotions rioting out of control, desperate to escape from the environs of his office, and the forceful presence of him.

She struggled to her feet, gasping in pain when Jake's fingers closed over her wrists, dragging her against him as he strode round to her side of the desk.

'Enough? No way,' he grated, transferring one hand to her chin and forcing her head backwards until Kelly thought her neck would snap under the strain.

'Although it's very gratifying to see that you're joining the human race again, Kelly, becoming a woman again.' He touched her hair and Kelly shuddered, her mind betraying her completely. Jake was only inches away. She could see the dark beard shadowing his jaw, smell the masculine scent of his skin. Her body ached to be held close against him, to be caressed and kissed.

She shuddered deeply, perspiration breaking out on her forehead. 'Let me go, Jake.' Her voice sounded odd and husky. 'I don't know why you brought me here . . .'

'You mean you think you know, but you're wrong, Kelly. I'm not so hard up for a woman that I need to procure them by force!'

'I know that!' She almost spat the words at him,

remembering the blonde girl and Jake's affection-
ate leavetaking of her at the airport, only hours
after she herself had lain in his arm, thinking they
were sharing something special and precious, but to
him all she had been was a challenge. She felt a
wave of familiar sickness, remembering the gloat-
ing look on Jeremy's face when he told her.

'All right, Kelly, I'll tell you what you're doing
here.' He released her and returned to his desk,
opening a drawer and removing several photo-
graphs which he placed purposefully on the desk.

Kelly stared at them. They seemed to be of an old
baronial building of some kind.

'I don't know how much you know about my
family—probably very little, because my father
shuns public life, but at one time our family owned
the Isle of Marne, off the west of Scotland. We lost
it before the First World War, but it then came up
for sale and my father bought it. This . . .' he
tapped the building in the photograph with one
long forefinger, 'was once a pele tower—later
embellished and embroidered into what it is today,
and my father has decided he wants to turn it into
an exclusive holiday retreat for exhausted business-
men. He's getting concerned about the fact that he
isn't yet a grandfather,' he added sardonically, 'and
I suspect this is his way of bringing that fact home
to me. He promised me the house and the island
for a wedding present,' he added, watching her
with what Kelly could only interpret as deliberate
cruelty.

'Perhaps you'd get to the point,' she interrupted
coldly. 'I didn't come here to listen to a potted
version of your family history, Jake.'

'God, to think I thought . . .' His jaw clamped on whatever he had been about to say, and he said instead, 'The point is, Kelly, that my father wants to consult a PR firm about the best way of bringing the hotel into prominence. He asked me if I could recommend a PR company who could handle the job.'

'And you recommended me?' Kelly couldn't keep the astonishment out of her voice.

'Why not?' Jake drawled, suddenly very much in control of himself. 'Call it payment for services rendered, if you like.'

Kelly went white.

'What's the matter?' he jeered unkindly. 'Or is it a different matter when you're the one who's on the receiving end of the insults?

'Where are you going?' he demanded when Kelly stood up shakily, reaching for her bag.

'Back to London,' she told him curtly.

'Running away? I expected better of you, Kelly. You know what I think?' he mused softly, 'I think you're frightened, Kelly; frightened of being a woman; frightened that you're not, after all, indifferent to me.'

'Of course I am.'

'Are you?' He asked the question smoothly, not giving her the opportunity to reply before he added, 'Then why run away? Your company is successful, Kelly, but not so successful that it can afford to turn down good business, and without even making the slightest effort to secure it. What would the rest of your Board say to that, I wonder? Something tells me they wouldn't like it.'

Kelly knew that he was quite right. She ran her tongue over her lips nervously.

'I'm not saying I'm not interested in the contract—merely that I suspect the motive for being offered a chance to tender for it.'

'Tell me, Kelly, have you ever trusted anyone?' She swallowed painfully, hating the cynical contemptuous look in his eyes. 'You can't spend the rest of your life punishing the whole world because one man let you down.'

'Haven't you done enough?' Kelly demanded, unable to keep up the façade of indifference any longer, aching with the need to reach out and touch him and hating him because of the way he had deceived her.

'Stop living in the past,' Jake told her ruthlessly. 'Prove to me that you've rejoined the human race. Prove to me that you're indifferent to me,' he added in a different tone. 'I'm flying out to the island tomorrow, I want you to come with me. My father is anxious to get things under way as quickly as possible. He can't handle it himself because he's tied up with talks with the Energy Minister. For God's sake,' he muttered, when he saw her face, 'do you think it's easy for me? Damn you, Kelly, don't you think I have any feelings?'

What could she say? If she said that he couldn't have any feelings and have treated her the way he had, he would guess how she felt about him.

'Your feelings are no concern of mine, Jake,' she managed at last, raising her head to add defiantly, 'and if tendering for this contract is what it takes to convince you of that, then that's what I'll do!'

CHAPTER NINE

SHE wasn't going to let Jake see how frightened she was, Kelly decided grimly, staring blankly ahead of her as the small aircraft gained height, and the mist that had greeted her when she woke up that morning pressed heavily against the cabin windows.

If she had had any sense she would have refused to come on this trip with Jake, but her pride wouldn't let her back down, not when he had come to collect her at her hotel this morning, smiling mockingly at her when she glanced hesitantly outside.

Now somewhere below them was Edinburgh and they were heading north to the Western Isles. Jake was sitting with the pilot and Kelly was free to study him unobserved, her heart aching as she remembered how he had deceived her. And he didn't even have the grace to apologise!

Why had he recommended her company to his father? As a means of making some kind of amends, or was his reasoning more subtle? Could he have guessed how she felt about him? Did he perhaps want to add to her torment? Why should he, she asked herself, but then why should he have deliberately allowed her to believe he was connected with the escort agency; why had he allowed her to think he was virtually penniless; why had he made love to her when Kelly had seen with her own eyes that there was someone else in his life? Pride prevented her from demanding answers to these questions, the same pride that had forced her into agreeing to accompany him this morning.

'Feeling all right?'

He turned quickly, catching her off guard and the dizzy weakness that filled her when he smiled told Kelly the real reason she had come with him. She still loved him!

'Kelly, are you all right?'

His voice sharpened and just for a moment Kelly allowed herself to think he might actually be concerned about her, quickly banishing the thought as she realised how improbable it was.

'I'm fine,' she told him huskily. 'How long does the flight take?'

'Twenty minutes or thereabouts, depending on the weather. Mists like the one we're seeing today can delay things a little.'

'Tell me a little more about the island,' Kelly suggested, forcing herself to sound businesslike. 'How did it originally come into the hands of your family?'

'It was originally owned by a Scottish arm of the family who were wiped out by Cumberland shortly after Culloden. The island was given to my ancestors by King George out of gratitude for supporting him instead of Bonnie Prince Charlie—it's remained in our family ever since. It's said that the original building was erected when Mary, Queen of Scots returned to Scotland from France, by an ancestor of ours who had been there with her at court. The original watch tower was extended and embellished in what is almost typically Scottish/French—lots of turrets and towers, the same sort of embellishments favoured by the French at the time. In fact, in those days the Scots, or those of them who made up Mary's court, were considered far more civilised than their English neighbours. During some restoration work ten years or so ago some documents were found relating to various purchases made for the castle; tapestries, carpets, all very expensive luxuries in their time. One wonders where a Highland laird found the money for them. It's rumoured that he was one of Mary's favourites. Whether that's true or not I don't know, but he certainly married well—a rich French heiress, and it was his son who founded the English side of the family. He quarrelled with his father and ran away from home. He joined Drake, became a staunch Protestant and found favour in Elizabeth's court.'

'It must be fascinating to be able to trace your family back so far,' Kelly responded eagerly, forgetting caution and doubt as she listened to Jake. A streak of romanticism, deeply hidden during the years since Colin, suddenly surfaced, and her face was unknowingly alight as she begged Jake to tell her more.

'My father's the one to talk to if you want to hear about the family history. It's his hobby, and he devotes most of his spare time to it. I think he's found considerable solace in it these last few years since my mother died. They were very close.'

Suddenly Kelly felt tears sting her eyes; not so much for the words as for the expression on Jake's face; shuttered, aloof, as though he were deliberately excluding her from something private.

'When my father complains because I haven't provided him with any grandchildren yet, I remind him that he didn't marry until he was well into his thirties. My parents' marriage was one of the fortunate ones. They say if your parents are happily married it adds to your own chances of marital happiness. Perhaps because it makes you far more selective, more demanding both of your partner and yourself.'

Kelly didn't know what to say. Was this some subtle way of pointing out to her that she did not fulfil his requirements? A way of reminding her that she fell far short of his standards?

She regarded him levelly and forced a cool smile. 'You'll have to be careful you don't turn into a crusty old bachelor, then, won't you?'

Jake's soft, 'Oh, I don't think there's much chance of that,' tormented her long after he had lapsed into silence. Was the blonde girl she had seen him with on Corfu a prospective bride?

'If you look down now you'll catch a glimpse of Marne.'

Jake's voice interrupted her miserable reverie and obediently Kelly glanced out of her window, her stomach lurching uncomfortably as a sensation of giddiness swept her, her eyes registering a small patch of greeny-grey dotting the steel blue sea, before she tore her glance away.

Jake watched her shudder unsympathetically.

'What's the matter?' he teased. 'Don't you trust the pilot? You know your trouble, Kelly?' he added sardonically. 'You've forgotten how to trust.'

'Perhaps it's just as well,' Kelly retorted bitterly. She had trusted him, hadn't she, and look where that had got her. She had even been ready to commit herself to him completely; to share with him everything she possessed; her money, the company. That was a laugh; compared with his wealth hers was a mere nothing, and yet he had deliberately let her believe that he was poor.

'If you suffer from vertigo, you'd better close your eyes now,' Jake warned as the small plane started to dip. 'The airfield is tiny, which is why we're using this particular type of plane. There's nothing to worry about,' he reassured her with a grin. 'It can land on a postage stamp—almost!'

Kelly felt the pilot was almost intent on proving the veracity of Jake's statement when she saw the tiny triangle below which Jake assured her was the airfield. As they dropped lower she had her first glimpse of the castle—not gaunt and severe as she had imagined, but delicate, sculptured out of stone, into a fairytale confection of turrets and towers, gilded by the sun suddenly breaking through the mist.

The tiny airfield was deserted. Jake stepped nimbly out of the plane and waited for Kelly to follow, helping her down, the touch of his hand on her arm electrifying, her body pulsing hotly from the point of contact.

'Okay, John, you can pick us up this afternoon,' Jake told the pilot laconically. 'Say four o'clock. That should give us enough time to see everything. There's a Land Rover in the shed over here,' he told Kelly, directing her gaze to the building at the edge of the airfield. 'Come on.'

As they walked towards it Kelly heard the plane taxiing for take-off and turned automatically to watch it.

'Where is everybody?' she queried as Jake pulled

open the door of the rough stone building he had referred to as a 'shed'.

'What do you mean, "everybody"?' He eyed her sardonically. 'The island is uninhabited now—"everybody" is you and me, and we're both here.'

'You mean we're alone here?' Kelly asked.

'My, my, how Victorian you sound!' Jake mocked. 'What's the matter, Kelly? Not as sure of your ground here as you were on Corfu, is that it?'

Before she could query what he meant, he had disappeared inside the hut, and was opening the door to a rather battered Land Rover.

'The island hasn't been inhabited for the last twenty years. It's too small to support enough livestock to bring anyone a decent living. There used to be a few crofters, but the children drifted away when they left school and eventually the others either left or died. That's one of the reasons why my father is so keen on this luxury recreational hotel idea. He reckons the island could provide a decent golf course. There's sea-fishing and a small inland loch; there's a grouse moor, although it's sadly denuded of birds at the moment. Someone comes over from the mainland once a week to check the place over; turn on the heating and give it an airing, that sort of thing, but my father wants to see it lived in.

'Come on, get in,' he ordered, opening the passenger door, and numbly Kelly went to join him.

There was no reason why the fact that they were the only two inhabitants of the island should unnerve her so much; it wasn't even as though they were intending to spend the night there, and even if they were she was perfectly safe from Jake. Her face burned as she remembered her response to his lovemaking, the unexpected sensuality he had revealed to her when he touched her.

It took just over ten minutes to drive to the castle. They entered it via a raised portcullis, driving into what had once been the keep but was now a garden with open cobbled spaces and a quantity of heathers and clumps of saxifrage.

'This garden was my mother's,' Jake explained curtly as he parked the Land Rover on the cobbles. 'She and my father lived here for a few years and then her brother, my uncle, was killed in a sailing accident one summer. After that, she couldn't bear to live here any longer.'

'You must have missed all this.' Kelly's glance encompassed the beauty of the cream stone, timelessly elegant, a child's dream; but Jake shrugged.

'I was away at boarding school most of the time. My parents moved to London. It was more convenient for my father's business interests. It's only been in these last few years that our petro-chemical interests have made moving our head office to Edinburgh a viable proposition.

'I'll show you over the place, and then we'll drive round the island, let you get the feel of it.'

'Jake, why did you suggest us—me—to your father for this, and I know you must have done?' Kelly continued, not letting him interrupt, 'because in his terms we're a very small concern indeed. I doubt he would even have heard of us.'

Jake didn't bother to deny her comment and Kelly shivered in the cold breeze which had sprung up suddenly, wishing she hadn't asked the question.

'Why?' he said harshly at last. 'For God's sake, Kelly, use your imagination! It shouldn't be hard to guess.'

He was gone before she could retort, striding across the cobbles and flinging open the arched oak door, heavily studded, and creaking in the authentic matter.

What did he mean, 'use your imagination'? Did he mean she ought to be able to guess that he was making some form of atonement, an apology without words, but that wasn't borne out by his behaviour which had swung from coldly cynical to barely restrained anger ever since they had met in the foyer to his office. He had known she was coming to Edinburgh; he had been prepared for their confrontation, whereas she . . .

She shivered again, telling herself that she mustn't allow herself to get caught in the same trap twice. This time she had no excuse; this time she knew that Jake wasn't interested in her as a person and never had been. At best she had merely been a 'specimen', an outdated freakish object in these permissive times, but he had been surprised when she told him that she was still a virgin and his lovemaking had been tender, or so she had thought at the time.

A gust of wind caught the open door, swinging it back with a bang. Kelly jumped, realising that she was alone in the courtyard. Telling herself firmly that she was here to do a job, and nothing else, she followed Jake into the house.

*

'And this is the Georgian wing,' Jake said drily, 'added by the same ancestor who was given the island by King George. He couldn't get a London architect up here, so he made do with a man from Edinburgh who had studied under Vanbrugh, and was by all accounts mightily pleased with the result.'

They were standing in a panelled library with uniform windows overlooking formal gardens.

'He wanted to knock down the original castle walls and give himself a better prospect, but his architect warned him that if he did, he'd be looking at barren earth. This side of the island catches the weather. Without the protection of the stone wall very little would grow.'

Privately, Kelly thought the formal garden was delightful. There was something very attractive about a walled garden, she decided, moving closer to the window. Perhaps because in her mind a walled garden was still connected with *The Secret Garden* which she had loved as a child. Modern-day educationalists probably didn't approve of such reading for children, she thought wryly, but she had certainly enjoyed it.

'We'd better take that drive now, I think,' Jake said behind her. 'The mist seems to be coming down again.'

Kelly hadn't noticed it, but he was right. The horizon was gradually blurring and she shivered, although in actual fact the library was quiet and warm.

'My father wanted you to see as much of the island as possible. No, we'll go out this way,' said

Jake, suddenly checking her as she turned towards the door.

His hand on her arm restrained her, her pulses thudding hectically, but Jake seemed unaware of her reaction as he indicated another door she hadn't seen. It led into a passage which brought them out at the back of the castle in the old and now deserted stable block.

'These buildings are soundly built and my father believes they can be converted into guest rooms.'

'But you don't agree with him?' Kelly said shrewdly.

'Well, let's say I had grown accustomed to thinking this place would be my home.'

'It still can be surely, if you marry,' said Kelly, remembering what he had told her.

'Mmm. You seem to like the house. How about taking me on with it?'

'The house I would enjoy, but you most definitely not,' Kelly lied quickly, bending her head so that he wouldn't see the betraying colour storming her cheeks. Her hand shook weakly as she reached for the door handle, but she was determined not to let him see how much his mocking comment had hurt.

'Why?' Jake almost snarled the word, his violence startling her, somehow intensified by the heavy mist pressing in on them. 'Because I remind you too much of Colin?' His mouth twisted. 'There's one regard in which I'm not like him, Kelly,' he told her brutally, the breath leaving her lungs on a painful gasp as he reached for her, fingers biting deeply into her arms as he held her against the length of his body, his mouth burning hotly against hers as he muttered, 'and that's this. He might not have wanted to touch you, but I damned well do!'

His mouth seemed to burn where it touched, her body on fire with an answering need, her fingers locking behind his neck, her heart thudding against the hard wall of his chest as he kissed her throat, the delicate shell of her ears, her eyelids, closed in mute ecstasy, and then the trembling softness of her lips, tracing their outline with his tongue, tasting them slowly like a connoisseur, before the harsh groan of his indrawn breath sent a shivering response through her, and they parted instinctively beneath the hungry pressure of Jake's.

An aeon, or was it only seconds, passed. Kelly was oblivious to everything but the possession of Jake's mouth, the controlled tension in his body which told her how much he wanted her. He broke the kiss, cupping her chin, his breathing harsh and ragged in the misty silence as he stared down at her.

'You want me, Kelly,' he said unsteadily, staring down at her. 'No matter what you told Benson, you want me.'

Kelly felt sick, instinctively pulling away. She might have told Jeremy in an effort to protect herself that she didn't want Jake, indeed she couldn't remember now what she had told Jeremy, but Jake had obviously seen her words as some sort of challenge. Waves of nauseous shivering racked her. This was how Colin had looked at her in those moments before he pushed her aside in disgust; angry and aroused, determined to force her to submit to him. Men hated being challenged where their sexuality was concerned, she should have remembered that.

'No!'

The sound was torn from her throat and she rushed headlong from the stableyard, not caring nor aware of where she was going. The gardens gave way to rugged hillside and scrub, the mist a thick wet blanket penetrating the cord jeans and warm jumper she was wearing. Behind her, she could hear Jake calling, but he sounded so angry that the sound of his voice only incited her to run faster. The ground rose sharply, and Kelly stumbled, catching her foot on a tussock of grass and falling heavily, the breath knocked out of her lungs, so that she was still lying on the damp hillside, fighting for breath, when Jake found her.

'Are you crazy?' he demanded roughly. 'You don't know a damned thing about the terrain here, you can't see more than a yard in front of you. You could have killed yourself! What the hell was all that about anyway?'

'I should have thought it was obvious,' Kelly managed icily between gulps of air. 'I didn't want you to touch me.'

'So you keep saying,' Jake agreed brutally, 'but your body says different. Can you manage to walk back to the castle? I'd carry you, but you don't want me touching you, do you?' he said sarcastically, glancing around as he straightened up. 'I think we're going to have to abandon our tour of the island. This mist is coming in fast and we wouldn't be able to see a thing.'

'Will the pilot be able to land?' Kelly asked. Her

teeth were chattering, her body shocked and cold.

'What's the matter? Afraid of being alone with me?'

'Certainly not,' Kelly retorted coldly. 'It's just that I told my office I'd be returning to London tonight.'

'No problem,' Jake assured her. 'If John can't land, he'll radio a message to us, and I'll have him radio one on to your office. Simple.'

With every step back to the castle the mist seemed to thicken. Kelly felt as though every bone in her body had been jarred by her fall. She ached in a thousand places and seriously doubted that she would have been able to find her way back without Jake. The mist cast an eerie atmosphere round the castle and she found herself shivering as Jake held open the main door.

'If you can wait half an hour I'll get the generator going and you can have a hot bath,' Jake told her laconically. 'You're soaked through.'

The mist hadn't penetrated his soft leather jacket, and Kelly wondered balefully if he had known what the weather was going to be like before they left Edinburgh. If so, he might have warned her. Her jumper seemed to have absorbed the damp rather than resisted it, clinging to her like a cold wet blanket.

'I'll pour you a drink and then I'll go and see about the generator,' Jake told her, walking her towards the library. A fire had been laid in the hearth and he knelt down, setting a match to it. 'Angus comes over every week to check the place over, and fortunately always leaves the fires ready.' He wanted for a few seconds until he was sure that the wood had caught, then got up lithely, walking towards one of the cupboards.

'Drink this,' he commanded, pouring some amber liquid into a heavy crystal tumbler. 'It's whisky,' he told Kelly when she stared at him rebelliously. 'Not enough to do you any harm, if that's what's worrying you, but it should take the chill off. Here.'

She took the glass, unnerved to discover how much her hands were shaking.

'Stay here by the fire, I won't be long,' Jake told her, watching her dispassionately for a few seconds before heading for the door. After it had closed behind him Kelly was startled to discover that she had been holding her breath. With Jake gone some of the tension drained out of her body, leaving it aching even more than before. Despite the whisky she was still cold, her jumper a wet soggy mass that seemed to clasp her with icy fingers, preventing her from gaining any benefit either from the fire or the whisky.

The lure of the flames proved too much and she inched nearer to their warmth, glancing anxiously at the door before tugging the wet jumper over her head and placing it on the hearth. She would hear Jake coming long before he reached the library— plenty of time for her to pull her jumper on again, and at least in the meantime she could have the benefit of the fire's warmth.

Gradually the blood seemed to seep back into her frozen body. Lulled by the warmth of the fire and the potency of the whisky, Kelly leaned back against a footstool. Jake had been gone longer than she had expected. Perhaps the generator was proving troublesome, she decided drowsily, barely aware that her eyes were closing.

When Jake opened the door she was soundly asleep, her skin gleaming silkily in the firelight. She didn't stir as he approached, the harsh planes of his face softening slightly as he watched her. He crouched down beside her, saying her name softly, his fingers tracing a line down her back.

Kelly opened her eyes, too comfortable and warm to move. She had been having the most wonderful dream. She had dreamed she was with Jake, in his arms. She sighed, stiffening as she realised where she was and that she wasn't alone, shock rippling through her as she realised part of it at least hadn't been a dream. She was in Jake's arms, her head pillowed against his chest, his fingers stroking softly along her spine. Her jumper! She stared helplessly at the hearth, cursing herself for falling asleep.

'Jake?'

'Don't talk,' he commanded thickly. 'Don't spoil it, Kelly.'

She was aware of him bending his head, of his lips against the back of her neck, awakening sensations she had tried to forget ever since she had returned from Corfu. His mouth moved downwards, lingering on each vertebra. Kelly felt him unfasten her bra, his hands cupping her breasts. Her body shook as she tried to withdraw, to cut herself off from the emotions his touch aroused, but it was too late; her body, weak and treacherous was already responding, overruling the dictates of her mind, and she was twisting in Jake's arms clinging wordlessly to him as his hands stroked over her body and it surrendered mindlessly to the pleasure of his touch.

'God knows how I've wanted this,' Jake muttered hoarsely against her throat, his hands on the waistband of her jeans, 'and you've wanted it to, Kelly, no matter how much you might try to deny it.'

She was past doing that; past doing anything but responding feverishly to his touch, her lips exploring the warm column of his throat, her body thrilling to the harsh sound of pleasure her touch elicited. And it was Jake who threw aside his jacket, ruthlessly tugging at buttons as he wrenched open his shirt, drawing Kelly down against him as he rolled on to the floor, placing her hands inside his shirt against the tangle of crisp hair darkening his chest.

His flesh tasted faintly salty against her tongue and Kelly shivered in pleasure as she felt his shuddered response, barely aware of him removing her jeans, totally engrossed in her delicate exploration of his body.

When Jake cupped her breasts, kissing the aroused peaks gently, desire cramped through her, her fingers curling into the waistband of his jeans as she fought to control her breathing, terrified of what her response might reveal to him, but it didn't seem to be enough to stop her from shaking like someone with a fever. And then she realised it was Jake who was shaking, his eyes dark with a passion which stirred her own senses, the brush of his tongue against her nipples making her abandon restraint.

He moved, rolling her underneath him, tugging

impatiently at his jeans, muttering something hoarsely under his breath, before he abandoned the attempt, guiding her hands to complete the task, his heart thudding against her like a sledge-hammer, making her own blood beat equally frantically.

His belly felt flat and hard, her tentative caresses eliciting a response that made Kelly ache with a need she had suppressed ever since her return from Corfu, only now she wasn't unknowing and inex-perienced and her responses were those of a woman, deeply desirous of a man intensely loved. The touch of Jake's fingers against her thigh in-voked a husky moan of protest, but he seemed not to hear, bending his head to savour the aching tips of her breasts, her whole body acutely attuned to his touch.

'Kelly, I'm not Colin.' His voice was slurred, his breathing raw and jagged, his mouth lifting from her breasts to her throat, her thighs parting instinc-tively as he moved against her, their hearts thud-ding in unison until the sound seemed to reverber-ate through the silence of the room.

Jake tensed, lifting his head, and then glanced at his watch. 'Damn,' he swore huskily. 'That's John back with the plane!'

Kelly pulled away, the spell woven by their love-making broken by the intrusion, reality crashing down on her as she reached hurriedly for her jumper.

'You wanted me, Kelly,' Jake told her harshly, as though he read her mind and wanted to impose upon it for all time his knowledge of her weakness.

She could have retorted that he had wanted her,

but men could want without love, women could not. As she pulled on her jumper she wondered what would have happened if she hadn't run away, hadn't got wet, hadn't taken her jumper off and then fallen asleep—and yet deep down inside, part of her refused to regret it; only that they had been interrupted when they had! In his arms, the fact that he had lied to her, made a fool of her, had meant nothing, and the knowledge of how easily her pride gave way to her love shocked and frightened her.

CHAPTER TEN

'OKAY, so it was too misty to see the island, but couldn't you have gone back? One or two of us are getting concerned, Kelly—both about you and the future of the company. Things aren't looking so good. We're in the middle of a recession and naturally enough the first thing people cut down on are the luxuries: the PR work and advertising. That contract was something we needed!'

Kelly stared disbelievingly at her oldest and most senior fellow director. Alan had said nothing to her of this when she left for Edinburgh. It was true that things were a little difficult at the moment, but surely nowhere near as serious as he was intimating?

'Look, Kelly, perhaps some of the blame lies with us. A few of us have seen what's coming, but we haven't wanted to worry you. In the last month we've had four cancellations—three while you were away in Corfu.'

Picking up the implied criticism Kelly replied drily, 'That was my first holiday in two years, Alan, but I take your point, even though I don't agree that you were right to conceal things from me. But now I do know we'd better call a board meeting to see how best we can put things right.'

'If they can be put right,' Alan Cormont said gravely. 'I don't want to be a wet blanket, Kelly, but I think we've a tough time ahead of us, the only consolation—if it is a consolation—is that we won't be alone.

'You look tired,' he added with belated consideration, his voice suddenly gruff as he added, 'You haven't seemed yourself for a while now, Kelly—ever since you came back from Corfu, in fact. Nothing wrong, is there?'

If only he knew! Kelly thought bitterly. She had left Edinburgh almost immediately the pilot had put down after the short flight back from the island, endured in a cold, gripping silence which left her too much time to think; to wonder what had possessed her, and worse, what Jake must have thought of her wildly abandoned response to him.

They had parted with brief, conventional words, and her heart had felt like a lump of lead in her chest ever since her return. And now Alan was berating her for not working harder to get the contract—a contract it seemed her company badly needed. The company, once the totally absorbing *raison d'être*, had taken second place in her life. She was worried about it, naturally, but nothing like to the extent she would once have been.

The headache which had been hovering all morning struck ferociously after lunch—a sandwich, eaten hurriedly at her desk and washed down with cold coffee—and on impulse Kelly decided to go home. She would worry just as efficiently there, she decided drily, gathering her bag and papers.

She was crossing Bond Street when she felt the hand on her shoulder. As she spun round quickly, her first thought was that someone was about to snatch her bag, but instead she found herself look-

ing into the smiling face of the girl she had last seen
at Corfu Airport with Jake.

'I thought it was you,' the girl exclaimed eagerly.
'I hope you don't mind me stopping you like that.
You may not remember me—Corfu, a party . . .'

'Yes, yes, I do remember you,' Kelly told her.
Her lips felt like cottonwool, her mouth unpleasantly dry as she tried to form the words without letting her lips tremble. 'You were . . . talking
to Jake.'

'Yes, he was pouring out his troubles to me,' she
agreed with a grin. 'Quite a role reversal! Look,
have you got time for a cup of tea? I'm Lyn, by the
way. I've heard all about your visit to Edinburgh
from Uncle Richard and I'm dying to know what
happened. Oh, I know you must think it frightfully
inquisitive of me—but you see, it was me who told
Jake not to give up. I was pretty sure you cared for
him. A woman can always tell better than a man,
can't she, and I was over the moon when my
godfather, Uncle Richard, wrote to say that Jake
had persuaded him to get you up there on some
pretext or other. Oh . . .' She stared uncertainly at
Kelly, who was motionless on the pavement, her
face totally devoid of colour. 'Oh dear, have I said
something wrong? You see,' she rushed on, 'I was
so sure you loved Jake, despite what he told me.
Oh . . .'

'I think that cup of tea was a good idea,' Kelly
interrupted firmly, trying to gather her wildly disordered thoughts.

They found a small café off Bond Street, blessed-
ly quiet after the lunch-time rush, and Kelly
ordered for them, wondering as she did so if she

was going mad, or had simply stepped into some sort of Looking Glass world.

'Now,' she said quietly when they had been served, 'let's start at the beginning. I saw you in Corfu, with Jake.'

'*With* Jake? You mean you thought Jake and I . . . Oh, no wonder you wouldn't have anything to do with him! Jake is almost an older brother to me. His father is my godfather and Jake has been marvellous, always helping me out of jams, you know . . . I got heavily involved with someone last year, I won't go into details, but when it all fell apart Jake was there to help me pick up the pieces. Every time we meet I always tease him, you know, ask him if he's met "the One" yet. This time he said "yes".' Lyn looked at Kelly. 'He told me how you'd met—all about you thinking he worked for the escort agency—oh, you mustn't mind, he let something slip by accident and I dragged the rest out of him. What a joke! I told him it was high time he realised how ordinary mortals live. Because his father is so rich a lot of women see him as a good catch, you know. I wanted him to introduce us, but he said he didn't want to panic you. He told me you didn't share his feelings.' She pulled a face and glanced hesitantly at Kelly. 'I thought differently, and I told him so. I was leaving Corfu in the morning and Jake promised to see me off. I told him then not to give up. He rang me a couple of weeks ago, and I asked him about you then. He told me things hadn't worked out. He was using that voice that says don't dare ask anything more, but I told him he was a fool if he let you go so easily. Was I right?'

Kelly managed a wan smile. 'Right and wrong,' she said shakily. 'Are you sure that . . .'

'That he loves you?' Lyn rolled her eyes heavenwards and laughed. 'Straight from the horse's mouth,' she confirmed. 'You know what Jake's like, close as the grave when he wants to be, but he did admit that he was worried about your reaction to the discovery that he wasn't some out-of-work actor and that he'd deliberately deceived you.' She grinned reminiscently. 'He actually unbent enough to admit to me that he fell in love with you on sight. He was just about to tell you that the agency had closed down and that he'd taken over the offices when he realised that if he did you would probably walk out of his life. He told me it was the most impulsive thing he's ever done.' She gave a gurgle of laughter. 'Poor Jake, you've certainly given him a run for his money! Not that it will do him any harm. Much as I love him there's no doubt about it—so far Jake hasn't had to try very hard when the feminine sex is concerned. But here I am prattling on without giving you a chance to say a word!

'Everything went well in Edinburgh and Jake got a chance to put his case. When he saw me off at the airport, he was so withdrawn and worried that I didn't want to ask him if he told you the truth.'

'When he was telling you about the agency,' Kelly asked her slowly, 'was anyone else with you?'

The other girl frowned. 'No. We were by the pool at the time, people all around us but no one actually with us—why?'

Perhaps something of her confiding manner had rubbed off on her, Kelly thought wryly, half

amused and half alarmed by her own need to admit
her doubts.

'It's just that a friend of mine told me that Jake
had told him the truth; had in fact boasted of how
he'd deceived me quite deliberately, and how . . .'
Kelly fought to steady her voice, 'how amusing it
would be to . . .'

'No! None of that's true,' Lyn cut in ruthlessly. 'I
know Jake. He would never do anything like that.
I'm not saying he can't be pretty miffy when the
mood takes him, but he's never cruel or vicious.
He's too male a man for that. But surely Jake
himself explained . . .'

'I left Corfu on the same plane as you,' Kelly told
her levelly.

'Oh, you mean you don't love Jake? I've
really gone and put my foot in it, haven't I?' Lyn
groaned.

'I do love him,' Kelly admitted huskily, 'and that
was one of the reasons why I left. You see, I
thought you and he—and then . . .'

'But you went to Edinburgh,' she interrupted.

'Yes,' Kelly agreed on a sigh. Was this girl right?
Did Jake love her? According to the younger girl he
had admitted as much to her, and Kelly knew
enough of Jeremy to guess that he could have
overheard their conversation and twisted it to his
own ends. He was bitter and envious enough to
have found pleasure in lying to her, but Jake? Why
hadn't he come after her when she left Corfu? Why
had he waited so long and gone to such lengths to
get her to Edinburgh? And he had been so bitter.
There were too many ends that just didn't tie up,
Kelly thought, chewing at her bottom lip, but she

already had an idea where she could unravel some of them.

'Look, do you mind if I rush off?' she asked quickly. 'There's someone I have to see.'

'And Jake?'

'Er . . .'

'He's due to arrive in London tomorrow. He has an apartment in the new Hartland block—more of a penthouse really. I was going to have dinner with him, but I can't make it.'

'I'll have to go,' Kelly told her, 'but thanks for telling me . . . everything.'

'Jake would probably kill me if he knew. I can't understand why he hasn't told you himself.'

'Perhaps he's decided he doesn't love me after all,' Kelly suggested in a shaky voice.

Lyn shook her head vigorously. 'No way,' she laughed. 'He loves you all right and, knowing Jake, it's a forever kind of love. That's the way he is.'

Jeremy's secretary answered the phone, putting Kelly through within seconds, and Jeremy's voice oozed satisfaction and self-esteem as he murmured her name.

'Has Sue been in touch?' he asked her. 'She's pregnant again, but this time the doc has told her to take things easy. I'm staying in town during the week to take some of the pressure off her.'

'Bully for you,' Kelly muttered sardonically under her breath. 'Look, Jeremy,' she told him curtly, 'I have to see you. There's something I want to ask you.'

'Well, well, and to think I thought you were never going to get round to it!'

Kelly had to grit her teeth to stop herself from bursting the bubble of self-assurance that surrounded him.

'Your place or mine?' Jeremy asked her.

'Neither,' Kelly told him, thinking quickly. 'What about the Savoy Bar?'

As she had suspected, Jeremy leapt at the suggestion of meeting her somewhere so prestigious and she managed not to retort when he said smoothly, 'Oh, of course, I was forgetting, it all goes down to expenses, doesn't it?'

'Look, Jeremy, do you want to meet me or not?' Kelly demanded, forcing herself to hold on to her temper.

'I'll meet you.'

Ten past seven. Kelly glanced impatiently at her watch. Where was Jeremy? Five minutes later she saw him walk into the bar, stopping to preen in the mirror. As different from Jake as chalk from cheese. Kelly felt a familiar stab of pity for her friend combined with contempt for Jeremy.

'Ah, there you are.' He bent his head and, guessing that he intended to kiss her, she sidestepped swiftly.

'This isn't a social occasion, Jeremy,' she said crisply. 'At least, not entirely. Cast your mind back to our holiday in Corfu if you will.'

She watched him frown as the waiter took their order and waited for him to leave before continuing. 'At that time you told me that you'd discovered that Jake had lied to me, pretending to work for an escort agency, while all the time he was an extremely wealthy man. You intimated that I represented some sort of challenge to him.'

'So?' Jeremy was watching her sulkily.

Kelly studied her drink for a few seconds. Her heart was thudding heavily—so much depended now on the gamble she was taking.

'So what, I wonder, did you tell Jake about me?'

She knew immediately that she had been right to gamble and that Jeremy had indeed said something to Jake.

'Oh, come on, Jeremy,' she pressed home her advantage. 'When Jake returned from the airport and found I'd gone he must have asked you where and why.'

'He may have said something,' Jeremy agreed. 'I told him we weren't your keepers. Sue was pretty upset—too upset to talk to him really, what with you rushing off.'

'So what did you say to Jake? Did you tell him I wasn't interested in him?' Kelly demanded, making a wild stab in the dark. 'Did you, Jeremy?' she demanded fiercely, watching the muscle twitch in his jaw and the nervous tic beneath his eye.

'He was like a madman,' Jeremy admitted sullenly, 'demanding to know where you were, what we'd said to you. I told him it was nothing to do with us.'

'Did you tell him what you said to me before I left?' Kelly asked sweetly.

Jeremy's face told her the answer.

'I ought to hate you, Jeremy, but you're simply not worth the effort. Poor Sue! What on earth has she done to be landed with a contemptible creep like you?'

'Bitch,' Jeremy muttered thickly. 'He's welcome to you!' He slammed his glass down and got up, shouldering his way through the press at the bar, leaving Kelly alone.

Jake was welcome to her, he had said, but did Jake still want her? Could she believe what Lyn had told her? Did she have the courage to believe it?

There was only one way to find out, she decided, getting up. She only hoped that her courage wouldn't fail her!

'Well, another day over.'

Kelly smiled at her assistant. 'Mmm.'

Darting Kelly a curious glance, the other girl started to tidy her desk. Kelly had been preoccupied all day, and yet there was an air of suppressed excitement about her, a glow that she hadn't seen before.

'Going anywhere tonight?' she asked idly as she headed for the door.

'Er . . . I may be.'

Would this outfit do? Kelly wondered, staring at herself in her full-length mirror. She had changed twice since getting home, delaying tactics even if they were heavily disguised, and now suddenly the outfit she was wearing, a silk dress in a pretty pastel pink which suited her colouring, over which she was wearing a soft silver silk jacket, seemed too dressy for a casual visit, but it was too late to change again. It was already after eight and if she left it much longer Jake might have gone out.

It took every ounce of courage she possessed to get in the taxi and give the driver Jake's address.

The huge office block looked cold and unwelcoming, the last batch of cleaners leaving as Kelly walked in.

A lift took her to the top floor, the doors opening on to a pale grey expanse of carpet and a curt sign reading 'Penthouse—private.'

Licking her dry lips, Kelly stepped out, crossing the carpet to ring the bell set into the marble wall.

An aeon seemed to pass before she heard any sound of movement, and as she heard the door chain rattle she had to fight down an urge to turn and flee. Panic filled her. What if she was wrong? What if Jake didn't want her? But it was too late now, the door was opening and she had a glimpse of Jake's towelling-clad back disappearing down a corridor as he called over his shoulder, 'Late as usual, Lyn! Come on in, then.'

With a tremendous sense of anticlimax Kelly followed him inside, closing the door behind her. Jake didn't stop walking until she had followed him into a huge living room, furnished in starkly masculine colours and shapes, greys and blues predominating.

'Sit down, then,' he commanded. 'I thought you weren't coming.'

'Did you, Jake?'

Her voice arrested his hand on its way to the decanter. He stiffened and straightened slowly, his face dark and inscrutable as he turned to look at her.

'Kelly?'

'I . . . I ran into Lyn the other day and . . .'

Oh heavens, she was making a complete mess of this! Why on earth had she mentioned Lyn? She could see Jake's face closing on her, his eyes hard and unreadable as he said hardly, 'I don't know that misplaced sense of pity brought you here, Kelly, but I don't need it. You know where the front door is,' he added curtly. 'Do us both a favour and use it.'

She wanted to cry out at the pain his words brought, stabbing a thousand needle-sharp wounds in her heart.

'Jake, please,' she whispered huskily.

'Jake, please what?' he mimicked harshly.

She couldn't ask him if it was true that he loved her; not in cold blood with him standing opposite her as an enemy. She was turning to leave when a tiny inner voice urged her not to give in, not to be so fainthearted. This was her whole life at risk and the quality of the happiness she would find in it.

'Jake, please answer me one question,' she managed calmly. 'Did you intimate at any time to anyone that you saw making love to me as a . . . a challenge?'

She could tell that her question wasn't what he had expected. His eyes narrowed and he watched her thoughtfully.

'Who told you that?' he asked at length.

Her mouth was dry with fear and tension. She longed to back down, but too much was at stake. She hadn't come all this way to take the coward's way out now.

'The same person who didn't explain to you why I'd left Corfu,' she told him evenly. 'Jeremy told me that he'd overheard you and Lyn talking. He deliberately misled me, allowing me to believe that you and Lyn were lovers.'

'Lovers?' Jake shook his head disbelievingly.
'But . . .'

'Jeremy played on my insecurities. He knew
where to hurt me,' she admitted simply, taking a
deep breath and holding it as she watched him
levelly and said calmly, 'He knew I loved you.'

The silence lasted so long she began to despair,
to think she had gambled everything and lost, and
then Jake spoke, softly at first, and then more
harshly as he demanded huskily, 'You loved me?'

Kelly nodded her head. 'And still do,' she admitted. 'Surely you could tell by . . . by the way I
responded to you when you . . . when you made
love to me?'

There was a huge lump in her throat, but she
forced the words out, determined that she was not
going to lose him this time by default. He might not
love her, Lyn might be wrong, but she was still
going to tell him the truth.

'That first day,' Jake said slowly, 'God—I was
so furious with you! You walked into that office and
it was like seeing a dream come to life. You were
there, everything I'd always wanted, and then you
started to talk. You hated men—that came across
loud and clear, but you needed a man—an escort,
so I jumped in with both feet. I wanted you so badly
even then. Time enough later to tell you the truth,
when I'd gained your confidence, but everything
was so complicated. You'd been married—I
thought you must still be deeply in love with your
husband; and then there was Jeremy; and you kept
throwing my poverty in my face. Ridiculously, I
began to want you not just to love me, but to love
me as you thought I was.'

'I did,' Kelly interrupted softly. 'Oh, I fought against it, but when we were in Corfu I forced myself to face the truth; that I loved and wanted *you*. That night I tried to tell you; I woke up wanting to tell you, wanting to admit to you that you mattered more than anything else. I was so happy . . .'

'That you ran away?'

'Jeremy told me who you really were; he laughed about it and said you had done too. Try to understand, it was more than my shaky self-confidence could take. I ran away. I saw you at the airport with Lyn and that just seemed to confirm everything Jeremy had told me.'

'Oh, Kelly! I ought to beat you for misjudging me so badly. You really love me?' He cupped her face in his hands, studying each feature.

'So very much,' Kelly told him softly. 'I hoped and prayed that you would come after me, explain . . . make everything all right . . .'

'Jeremy told me you never wanted to see me again. He said you told him I reminded you of Colin—you can imagine what that did to me. All of a sudden you weren't making love with me, you were consummating a marriage to someone else. I told myself I hated you, but I was lying. I managed to last out about a month before I gave in and persuaded my father to get you up to Edinburgh. I thought once I got you to myself on the island, we could work things out, I could prove to you that it was me you were responding to, not some shadow.'

'That was why you were so angry! I thought it was me—something I had said or done; I thought you must be laughing at me, knowing how I felt about you, and then I bumped into Lyn in London and she told me you loved me, and I couldn't believe it. I went to see Jeremy, guessing that if he'd lied to me he could well have lied to you as well. You were never a substitute for Colin,' she told him huskily. 'Everything I told you that night was true. I never really loved him, I've grown to see that over the years, but the scars he inflicted stopped me from making other relationships, from being able to trust, until I met you and I fell so hard that I couldn't help myself.'

'That's a very tempting admission,' Jake drawled, and Kelly was suddenly aware that all he had on was his robe, and that he was regarding her with a very disturbing glint in his eyes.

Her breathing suddenly changed, she murmured huskily, 'Meaning?'

'Meaning that for the first time since we've met I can hold you in my arms like this, without any deceit between us, and I can kiss you like this—' he bent his head, brushing her lips with his until she was clinging dizzily to his shoulders, her breath coming jerkily from half parted lips—'without feeling that you're thinking of Colin, or worse still, Jeremy. And I can touch you like this,' he muttered throatily, sliding his hands beneath the thin silk of her jacket, finding the full curves of her breasts and caressing them urgently as he drew her against his body, kissing her with feverish intensity, showing her without the need for words that everything Lyn had said was true.

'I love you, Kelly,' he told her thickly at last, releasing her throbbing mouth to trace a line of kisses downwards, slowly unfastening the tiny buttons closing her dress. 'So much that it's an ache in my guts. I fell in love with you on sight, and then you nearly destroyed me with your ice-cold reserve, but I knew there was a living, warm woman inside somewhere, and I was determined to find her.'

'And now that you have?' Kelly whispered, shivering delicately with the pleasure of his marauding mouth, tracing pathways over her breasts.

'Now that I have she isn't going to escape until she's promised to make an old man very happy— my father's heard all about you from Lyn and he says if I don't return to Edinburgh with you beside me, I can definitely forget about Marne *and* the chairmanship of the company. He admits that it's far harder to persuade a woman to change her mind than it is to run a company, but he says I'm not the right man to fill his shoes if I can't. Not that he's really thinking of vacating them—at least not until we provide him with a brace of grandchildren.

'Will you marry me, Kelly?' he asked roughly in a different tone. 'Will you?'

She raised herself on tiptoe, twining her arms round his neck, drawing his head down until she could reach his lips, murmuring her assent against them, feeling her body take fire from his as he tensed in response, letting her take the initiative until, with a groan, he pulled her tightly against him and her body melted into his, alive with the pleasure of the contact, revelling in the hardness of him against her without the barrier of his robe, her response urging him to swing her up in his arms and carry her—not to the bedroom, but to the fire, where the lamplight played revealingly over his features as he placed her carefully on the floor, bending tenderly over her as he drawled unsteadily, 'This time there aren't going to be any interruptions—I hope!'

'Well, they certainly won't come in the form of planes landing,' Kelly agreed with a chuckle. 'Oh, Jake,' she whispered urgently, 'love me, please love me!' She reached up to pull him down against her, revelling in the tenseness of his body, the fine film of perspiration dewing his skin, the hungry pressure of his mouth as it possessed hers, obliterating all that was past and welcoming the future.